Religion, Healing and Health

THE MACMILLAN COMPANY
NEW YORK · BOSTON · CHICAGO
DALLAS · ATLANTA · SAN FRANCISCO

MACMILLAN AND CO., LIMITED
LONDON · BOMBAY · CALCUTTA
MADRAS · MELBOURNE

THE MACMILLAN COMPANY
OF CANADA, LIMITED
TORONTO

Religion, Healing & Health

By JAMES DALE VAN BUSKIRK, M.D.

THE MACMILLAN COMPANY

New York 1952

mental health

DEDICATED

to Those Who believe in Religion and would understand the Scientific Basis for its use for Healing and for Health of Body and Soul

FOREWORD

THIS BOOK is written to urge the value of religion, to encourage its use in maintaining good health of body and mind, and to point out the scientific basis for belief that religion has curative power in many ills and is preventive of some disorders. Religion is a vital need for wholesome, healthy living; but it is too much neglected as a help in healing and for health.

The use of religion for healing and health is not a magical, miraculous thing. It is based on well-recognized facts of physiology and psychology. Like the practice of personal hygiene, one can do better when he understands the how and the why, instead of just following rules and directions. Understanding of the physiology and pathology of the emotions should help us to avoid many ills and to regain health when we have had nervous disorders arising out of emotional disturbances or complexes.

This book differs from most of those urging the use and practice of religion for peace of mind and health, in that it emphasizes the scientific basis. The first part of the book is given over to the presentation of the underlying facts: the relation of body and mind and their mutual influence, the physiology and pathology of the emotions, how emotions may bring on sickness. Then we have a discussion of some of the ways of faith healing, both non-religious and religious, and some of the healing cults. I believe all this should lead to an understanding of the place of religion, as one of the most powerful emotions, in healing and for good health. But religion is not only an emotion, it is a philosophy of living; and there can be no philosophy without understanding. Religion is not a capricious thing of rules and ceremonials; the God of religion is the God who ordained the laws of science. I have thus given much space to this underlying science.

I have tried to show the non-professional reader the psychic causation of much of the common illness to which people are subject, the effects of unhealthy emotions, tensions, and attitudes on the body as well as on mental health. Fears, anxieties, worries, anger, resentments, hate, hostility, shame, and guilt, all affect both body and mind. These can be overcome by faith, trust, confidence, goodwill, love, forgiveness, reconciliation, and a genuine religious experience of the love and power of God. This puts religious help in healing, and for healthy living, on a sound scientific basis. Understanding these principles should help folk to gain insight as to what is causing some of their ills, and what to do about them. Many people have gained insight and overcome their wrong emotions and attitudes, by wholesome faith and love—faith in God and in our fellowmen, and love of God and of our neighbors.

I suppose no one sees more clearly than a doctor the great amount of suffering and disease brought on by anxiety, worry, fear, conflict, hostility, guilt, immorality, dissipation, and ignorance. William S. Sadler, one of America's leading medical men, says that more than half the afflictions of mankind could be prevented by right religious living: "The sincere acceptance of the principles and teachings of Christ with respect to the life of mental peace and joy, the life of unselfish thought and clean living, would at once wipe out more than one half the difficulties, diseases, and sorrows of the human race. . . . Irrespective of the future rewards of religion, laying aside all discussion of future life, it would pay any man or woman to live the Christ-life just for the mental and moral rewards it affords here in this present world." [1]

I have tried to emphasize the practice of religion rather than its beliefs, genuine faith rather than assent to creeds, the experience of religion rather than theology. Our faith in a law-abiding universe with spiritual reality at its center is a religious faith, when we accept it so truly that we live in confidence that the universe is friendly, because God is at the heart of it. I believe with Sadler that "personal religious experience is the highest and truest form of psychotherapy." The therapeutic value of religion is in living such a life of faith that fears and anxieties are overcome; that doubts and despair give way to trust and hope; such love of God and man that anger and hate are lost in goodwill and in the joy of fellowship; such an experience of the abiding presence of God that guilt loses its bitterness as we feel His reconciling love and are led into love and charity with our neighbors.

I do not consider that I have exceptional qualifications for the writing of such a book, but I deeply feel the need for it. I am a graduate in medicine, and have had a particular interest in psychology and psychosomatic medicine; and I am also an ordained minister. I have been active in church work about all my life, as a youth in my own church and in young people's organizations, and as a medical missionary in Korea for twenty-three years; I have also had experience as a pastor. It is probable that I see psychosomatic medicine and religion both from a somewhat different viewpoint from that of most of my colleagues in medicine and in the ministry. This book grew out of a series of talks and discussions with a church group of young adults; hence the primary emphasis of the

[1] William S. Sadler, *Modern Psychiatry* (C. V. Mosby Co., Saint Louis, Mo., 1945), p. 760.

book is an attempt to help religious people realize the values of religion for health and, as they achieve some insight into the relation of body and mind, what religion can do for health and healing.

I have not been concerned about originality as an author; I have drawn from medical and religious literature, as well as my own experience, for concrete facts and illustrations that confirm the scientific basis of my thesis that religion is of value for healing and for health. I am reluctant to cite personal case histories of my patients; and where I have done so, I have tried to avoid giving any facts that would identify anyone. I have condensed and adapted case histories and discussions of other writers, partly because they have already been made public, and because they illustrate and enforce the points I have tried to make, even better than things I might take out of my own experiences.

CONTENTS

xi

Religion, Healing and Health

1

Body and Mind

IT IS MY FIRM CONVICTION that sane, true religion, as taught and practiced by Jesus Christ, is vital to the health of the whole man, for the good life of body and soul; and that religion can be curative and preventive of much of the illness that afflicts people today—as always. I believe that the curative, health-giving power of wholesome religion is being sadly neglected. My medical studies and practice, and my religious experience, both confirm me in this conviction of the importance of religion for healthy living, for the cure of the sick, and for the prevention of much suffering.

If I were to take a text—as a minister may do—it would be the words of the Apostle Paul: "Your body is a temple of the Holy Spirit . . . glorify God therefore in your body." [1] These words indicate the religious significance of the body, and the ever-present power of God in us. Along with these words, I would like to use some from the modern psychiatrist, Jung, showing his idea of the importance of religion for bodily health: "During the past thirty years, people from all the civilized countries of the earth have consulted me. . . . Among all my patients in the second half of life—that is to say, over thirty-five—there has not been one whose problem in the last resort was not that of finding a religious outlook on life. It is safe to say that every one of them fell ill because he had lost

[1] I Cor. 6:19–20.

1

that which the living religions of every age have given to their followers; and none has been really healed who did not regain his religious outlook." [2] He says that loss of religion made his patients ill, and that, in his practice, religion was essential to a cure. Jung is not alone in this view: psychiatrists and psychologists have to deal with the inner spiritual life of man, the "psyche"; many of them are frankly telling patients they need to consult a minister. Physicians in general practice find that much of their work is due to spiritual problems—even though they do not use that word to tell their patients what is wrong with them. Ministers are finding that spiritual conditions cause bodily ills among their parishioners.

THE RISE OF PSYCHOSOMATIC MEDICINE

Doctors are now saying that about half (and some say more than half) of the patients coming to their offices have illnesses that are in part or wholly due to emotional or psychic disorders: (1) Some of these patients have *no definite organic disease;* their sicknesses are purely mental or psychic. (2) There is a larger number who have *both organic pathology* and definite *emotional factors*, and both are involved in the disease process. This is the great field of "psychosomatic medicine"—diseases of "psyche" and "soma," mind and body. (3) There is another group in whom the *physical factors are dominant*, though an emotional or psychic element is also present; an emotional crisis may precipitate the attack or greatly aggravate the physical illness in these patients. (4) And of course, there are diseases that have *little or no psychic factor:* such as the bacterial and virus infections, chemical or physical changes in

[2] C. G. Jung, *Modern Man in Search of a Soul*, p. 264 (permission Harcourt, Brace and Co., New York).

the body that result in sickness, while tumors can hardly be classed as psychosomatic.

But even in the physical diseases, the mental and spiritual attitudes of the patient have much to do with the way he reacts to the physical disease processes, and may be the decisive factor in the alleviation or cure in many cases. Case histories showing this will be cited on later pages.

The importance of this emotional, psychic element in disease is now well established in medical science. But it was not so when I was in medical college somewhat more than forty years ago. Then the whole emphasis was physical and materialistic: disease was just a physical or chemical process gone wrong, whether because of bacterial or mechanical causation. Our scalpels were not sharp enough and our microscopes were not adequate to demonstrate this, but we expected ultimately to prove the purely physical and chemical basis of all disease. We thought all diseases, even mental disease—we did not then have "psychiatry"—were wholly the result of organic pathology, in the brain or other organ or organs. I can recall only one hint of anything other than purely physical disease during my medical student days: that was in a then new term for neurasthenia, "psycho-somat-asthenia"—"mind-body-weakness." And now the key word in medicine is "psychosomatic."

Nineteenth-century medicine considered itself purely a physical science: its basic assumption was the material causation of all disease; the psyche was deemed only a function of the body. But now medicine recognizes the psyche, not only as a factor in functional disease, but as an actual cause of pathological processes—disease. The neuroses are now known to be psychic in origin, and their cure must be by some form of psychotherapy, even if it be no more than confidence in the physician, inspired by his ability and assurance.

The psychic causation of physiologic phenomena like blushing, blanching in fear, thumping of the heart, weeping, vomiting or diarrhoea in emotional upsets, and such, are well known; these are temporary bodily changes. Prolonged emotional tensions produce a prolonged rise in blood pressure, or changes in the secretions and movements of the digestive tract, that may go on into actual cellular changes, the pathological processes of disease. As Weiss and English put it: Psychological disturbance may lead to Functional impairment, and this leads to Cellular disease and Structural alteration.[3] It appears to be proven that cellular changes do result from emotional causes, as well as from infection, from allergy, from endocrine imbalance, from metabolic disorders, from deficiencies in diet, or from mechanical causes. Some diseases are definitely psychogenic.

It cannot be doubted that psychiatrists and physicians practicing psychosomatic medicine are doing much to relieve and cure illness brought on or aggravated by emotional disturbances. And it is just as true that religion is relieving and curing many people. There is just as real healing by religious faith as there is by psychotherapy. This will be made clearer later, but let me say here that when we investigate the emotional disturbances that make folk ill and cause them to seek medical care, we find anxiety, fear, worry, resentment, anger, hate, guilt, and like emotions. These are traditionally the realm of religion, and it has always dealt with them. Only of late has medicine claimed to do anything about them; now psychosomatic medicine is giving attention to the whole man, mind

[3] Edward Weiss and O. S. English, *Psychosomatic Medicine*, p. 2 (W. B. Saunders Co., Philadelphia).

and body. It is my belief that neither the sick folk nor their doctors can afford to neglect religion in the cure and prevention of these illnesses. "Man has always stood in need of the spiritual help which his religion holds out to him. . . . Man is never helped in his suffering by what he thinks for himself, but only by revelation of a wisdom greater than his own. It is this which lifts him out of his distress." [4] The restlessness, nervous tension, fears and anxieties of our day call for spiritual treatment.

REALITY OF THE PSYCHE

The rise of psychosomatic medicine indicates that medical science is turning away from its materialistic bias. There has never been any denial of the reality of the body; and we must also assume a non-physical psyche, unless we are materialists denying any reality aside from the physical. Religion has always said that man is more than just a body; and now psychosomatic medicine recognizes both psyche and soma—mind and body.

While we do not know mind apart from body, we cannot accept the materialistic dogma that the "brain secretes thought as the liver secretes bile." There are physico-chemical changes in the brain accompanying thought and emotion; but we do not believe psychological processes are nothing more than "conditioned reflexes." Thought is more than physico-chemical changes, more than "incipient laryngeal articulations supplemented by certain subtle visceral reverberations." We cannot accept Watson's dictum that "thought is nothing but talking to ourselves." [5]

[4] C. G. Jung, *op. cit.*, pp. 277 f. (permission Harcourt, Brace and Co., New York).

[5] John B. Watson, *Behaviorism*, p. 191 (W. W. Norton & Co., New York).

Conditioned reflexes, as observed by the physiologist, are truly marvellous: animals conditioned to the ringing of a bell at feeding time soon learn to respond to the bell-ringing; in time, even without food their digestive juices will flow when the bell rings. And we human beings, too, have learned many conditioned reflexes—else indeed, our daily living would make impossible demands on us. But this does not mean that all we do and say and think is no more than "conditioned reflexes." There is a reality in creative thinking; emotions are more than responses to external or internal stimuli.

We know that certain glandular secretions affect personality: but we will not concede that glands determine personality. The effect of these secretions, hormones, is vividly shown in the case of the thyroid: children whose thyroid secretion is deficient are dull, apathetic, and may even be imbecilic; but when given thyroid extract to make up for the deficiency they become bright, active children. Deficiency of thyroid in the adult makes him sluggish and dull. Adults whose thyroids are too active secrete too much hormone, become excessively nervous; removal of the excess thyroid brings them back to normal, as do certain drugs that inhibit thyroid secretion. Other glands definitely affect personality as well as produce changes in the body: the hormones of the sex glands in men make them masculine, and female hormones produce femininity in women; the changes in hormone production at the climacteric or menopause result in personality changes, sometimes to a profound degree.

Yet we cannot accept any thesis that makes even hormones the final determinants of character and personality. We see the psyche as the dominant partner; the mind and the emotions definitely alter the secretions of hormones; fear or anger causes a great increase in the secretion of the adrenal glands;

adrenalin; emotional stress seems to cause thyroid over-secretion in many cases. Chronic emotions produce chronic changes in secretions and definitely alter personality. Thus while glands affect personality, the personality, the psyche, affects the glands.

All of us know that we are moved to thought and action by external and internal stimuli—some of it very vaguely recognized, or even quite unconscious. The odor of delicious food stimulates appetite and promotes the flow of digestive juices, and prompts us to go and get the food; other odors may inhibit appetite and secretions. There are definite drives or urges innate in us; we are driven by forces that affect us, by what has happened to us and in us. But there is also something that pulls us; we strive toward something; we are not always driven. I believe that purpose or goal is at least as important in our living as the drives, the stimuli that set up our conditioned reflexes. This purposiveness is the mark of the mind, the psyche. This means that mind is determinant, that the psyche occupies the governing position in life. The higher we are in the scale of life, the more goal and purpose become dominant.

In the lowest forms of life there seems to be little, if anything, more than reflex processes; the organism is passive, it has to wait for some external stimulus and responds only in very simple ways: this is true even as to food-getting. But as we look at higher forms of life, we find increasingly complex and unpredictable responses to external stimuli; and the higher animals initiate action. There is progress from the purely physiological to the psychological as we go up the scale of living creatures. Emotions and will become, if not actually all-controlling, at least major factors in determining and in initiating human behavior.

The responses to stimuli in a small child are like reflexes only. But the adult determines the responses he will make in accord with his ideals and character, the goals he has set for himself. He does not save himself when love is in his heart; he goes on heroically in spite of suffering even to death. The martyrs of the ages bear witness to the dominance of spirit over body. There is truly more than physico-chemical processes and conditioned reflexes in man. "Science points to this supremacy and liberation of the mind as the goal towards which nature is working" (Hadfield [6]). Man is body *and* mind: "Both body and mind are expressions of life; they are parts of the whole of life" (Adler [7]). There is some justification for saying, "I have a body," rather than, "I am a body." But I prefer to say, "I am mind *and* body"; I believe that the "I" becomes increasingly independent of the body, and will continue to exist even after the dissolution of the body—death.

But what about "mind," "spirit," "soul"? Is man a three-fold being, or only a duality? There are differences in the meanings of these words—rather different emphases. But I see no reason to assume that man is three-fold: body, and mind, and soul or spirit. To me the words mind, soul, spirit, refer to different aspects of the non-physical, the psyche. This is consistent with good religious teaching, and it is the basis for psychosomatic medicine.

INFLUENCE OF BODY ON MIND

All of us know by experience how great is the power of body over spirit: how miserable, depressed, irritable we are when we have not had good sleep and rest, or are hungry.

---

[6] "The Mind and the Brain," in Burnett H. Streeter and others, *Immortality*, p. 71 (The Macmillan Co., New York).

[7] *What Life Should Mean to You*, p. 25 (Grosset & Dunlap, New York).

It is hard to be cheerful and optimistic when we have bad colds or the "flu"; headaches change our outlook on life. Poor health makes for poor work and mental depression; we are not efficient either physically or mentally when ill. The old Latin saying, "Mens sana in corpore sano" ("sound mind in a sound body"), expresses a real truth, in spite of glorious exceptions of great spirits that have overcome the handicap of weak, sick bodies: such as Louis Pasteur, Charles Darwin, Robert Louis Stevenson, Edward Trudeau, and many others among the great we all honor.

It is well known that undernourished children easily become problem children; they do better school work and have better dispositions when given adequate food. It has been shown that their "I.Q." will improve with improved nutrition. This same fact is well illustrated by the change in disposition of a group of "conscientious objectors" who submitted to an experiment in semi-starvation during their service in lieu of military duty: this group of young men were high-principled, peaceful college-age fellows, but after they had endured hunger and malnutrition for a while they became irritable, querulous, depressed, and had a hard time to keep peace among themselves.

I am sure we do Him injustice if we always picture Jesus as a man of sorrows, carrying grief. He did take our sorrows upon Himself, and He did suffer, but He was a man of good humor, cheer, and joy. The very fact that little children and their mothers were attracted to Him attests His wholesome manhood and joyousness. He was no pale, sickly, sad-faced Galilean; He had a smiling religion, a religion of healthy-mindedness. He began His Sermon on the Mount by talking about happiness: "blessed," or "happy," was its first word and its key-note. I have always been grateful to the preacher

who warned us as youths against thinking that it was religious
to be gloomy and sad, when it might be only dyspepsia: religion is not long-faced.

This preacher, Dr. Matt S. Hughes, afterwards a bishop
of the Methodist Episcopal Church, illustrated this point with,
for me, a never-forgotten story: A visiting minister one Sunday morning dragged himself into the pulpit looking sad
and discouraged; his sermon was as gloomy as he looked; even
his pulpit prayer began by calling himself and the congregation "poor worms of the dust." At the close of the service,
a good sister told her husband to bring the preacher to their
home for Sunday dinner, for, she said, he needed a good meal.
The husband did as he was told. After a good dinner and
visit in their home, that night the minister went up into the
pulpit like a conqueror; his evening prayer began with thanks
to God that we are "but little lower than the angels." So great
was the effect of a good dinner in a good home that it lifted
him from a "poor worm of the dust" to "little lower than the
angels."

I must also briefly refer to changes in personality that occur
in persons who have had a disease of the brain: very efficient,
high-principled men sometimes deteriorate mentally, socially,
in personal habits and in morality; often friends may note
the very time the changes began; the circulation in the brain is
impaired, a slight "stroke" that did not result in paralysis may
cause "softening of the brain." Encephalitis—a virus infection
of the brain—is commonly followed by mental and character
changes.

It is undisputed by any who have knowledge of science
that the body does have a profound influence on the mind or
spirit. It is our duty to take care of our bodies and make them
as fit for fine spirits as they can be made. We have no right

to abuse our bodies; we should keep them clean and fit: "Glorify God therefore in your body." This makes for the good life for the whole man, body and soul.

INFLUENCE OF MIND ON BODY

The first and most obvious influence of mind over body is seen in our voluntary movements, where the mind, the will, initiates the processes that result in bodily movements. For example, while writing this, I thought of something I wanted to look up: I got up from my desk and walked to the bookshelf, found the book I wanted and read the passage desired. The initiative in this series of actions was mental: it was not just a "conditioned reflex," though many of the movements have become so habitual that one gives no thought to the particular actions. These movements are voluntary, controlled by the brain and the cerebro-spinal system; they originate in the psyche.

We cannot locate a "will center" in the brain; but the frontal lobe appears to be the place for thought processes— the center for the higher psychic functions. There is a definitely located motor center in the brain. This has been demonstrated by physiologists in their studies on animals—and in man during surgery when the skull is opened—by electrically stimulating the cortex in various parts and noting movements of the body that result. Study of the brain in patients who have died after having motor symptoms confirms the surgical findings. We know that nerve fibers pass from the brain to the spinal cord, and that other fibers convey the impulse to the muscles; thus the brain controls our voluntary movements.

There is another kind of control of the body by the mind: inhibition of movements, in contrast to stimulation. To illustrate: ordinarily when we wake and realize it is six o'clock (or your usual hour), the mind sets off the morning routine of getting up, washing, dressing, eating, and going to work; but if we wake and recall that it is a holiday, the routine is called off for a while. Doctors see patients inhibit movements every day: they hold still and allow us to cut open boils or other infections, instead of jerking away from the knife. Thus the psyche may inhibit the natural movements of the body even to the extent of great suffering and perhaps of martyrdom.

But there are muscles in our bodies that are not under this voluntary control. One will blush from shame and embarrassment in spite of the will and effort to avoid doing so. The cold sweat of fear is not amenable to control by the voluntary nervous system; fear or anger makes the heart beat faster in spite of our will—because of the emotion. Emotions register bodily changes through the autonomic nervous system: i.e., the sympathetic and parasympathetics. The autonomic system is not controlled directly by the brain: there are lower centers that may initiate complicated reflexes, as from pain or fear. But this system is not independent of the brain; there are connecting fibers by way of the spinal cord and mid-brain; so mental states and emotions positively affect the autonomic system. Thus mental work, like solving problems in mathematics, causes changes in the distribution of the blood; emotions result in physical changes, as in fear or shame, as mentioned above.

PHYSIOLOGY OF THE EMOTIONS

The autonomic nervous system may be aroused to action reflexly by stimuli that arise from within our own bodies; it may also be stimulated indirectly by things without the body, such as sights, sounds, odors, and anything causing pain; it is also excited by our emotions. It produces some changes in the body of which we may be conscious but over which we have no voluntary control; other changes occur of which we may not be conscious at all.

One cannot discuss the physiology of the emotions without relying upon the work of Cannon and the physiologists who worked with him in the Harvard laboratories. In some of their experiments they studied the bodily changes in cats subjected to emotional stress by the threats of a barking dog. Everyone knows how a cat's hair will stand up, from head to tip of tail; the pupils of its eyes will dilate; it will spit and growl at the dog; its muscles will grow tense, ready to fight or run away. The internal changes, in both humans and animals subjected to stress, are even more remarkable: the heart action is increased as to rate and volume output; the blood pressure goes up as the blood vessels of the abdominal area are constricted and more blood is forced to the heart to pump to the muscles and the brain. The bronchial tubes are relaxed to allow air to pass more easily to the lungs and supply oxygen to the blood. The spleen is contracted and its stored-up blood corpuscles are forced out into circulation; there are more blood cells in the blood, increasing its oxygen carrying power. The blood coagulates more quickly—this might be life-saving in case of injury in fight or flight. There is an increase in the amount of sugar in the blood: sugar is stored in the liver and the muscles in the form of glycogen; excitation of the sympathetic nerves causes a release of the stored glycogen and it is broken down into smaller molecules of glucose, the normal sugar of the blood. Muscular activity requires oxygen and glucose, and both are made freely available by the sympathetic system. At the same time, the normal movements of the stomach and intestines are inhibited, and the secretion of the digestive juices is reduced or completely inhibited—as if even digestion and nutrition must stop in the emergency. In addition to the direct action of the sympathetic nerves on the organs of the body, there is a further effect produced by the secretion of adrenalin, a hormone from the adrenal glands. The effect of increasing the amount of adrenalin in the blood is practically the same as that of the direct sympathetic stimulation, thus augmenting the sympathetic stimulation. There is such an intimate relation of the sympathetics and the adrenals that Cannon called it the "sympathico-adrenal system."

The nerves of the sympathetic system come from a chain of ganglia (clumps of nerve cells) along the spine and around the great blood vessels of the abdomen. These ganglia are connected to the spinal cord, and thus indirectly to the brain. From the ganglia the nerve fibers go to the stomach and intestines and the abdominal glands; other fibers go to the heart, to blood vessels, to the lungs, to the mouth and salivary glands, to the eyes, and to the muscles of the hairs. Thus the sympathetic nerves reach practically every organ of the body, a pathway for emotions to affect the entire body. The sympathetic nerves also convey sensory impulses from the organs to the centers—subconscious sensation; the sympathetic centers thus become centers for reflexes. The action of the sympathetic system is general, as a unit: it affects all the organs that it reaches; it does not act on heart or stomach alone, but on the whole group of organs. This is in contrast to the action of the voluntary nervous system: one can move one arm, or one finger, or one eyelid; the sympathetics all act together. (The parasympathetics also act on specific organs: eyes, heart, lungs, stomach, intestines, glands, or on groups of these organs.)

Besides the ganglia of the autonomic system, there is a higher center for them. If the cerebrum of animals is destroyed, leaving the base of the brain, the animals will show all the reactions of the autonomic system, all the signs of emotions such as rage or fear; but if the hypothalamus in the base of the brain is destroyed, the physical changes accompanying emotions cannot be induced. We see thus that the internal effects of the emotions are not dependent on the brain, but that the overt actions appropriate to the emotion are subject to the approval or inhibition of the higher centers in the brain, the psyche. Excitation of the hypothalamus prepares the body for active expression of emotions when released by the cortical centers. There may be overwhelming, impulsive emotional displays, uncontrolled by higher centers; these are thalamic manifestations. One may experience a conflict between the thalamic impulse to fight or to run, and the conscious desire to avoid giving way to the emotions. The natural impulse to action in accord with the primitive emotion may be restrained in accord with one's feeling of the proprieties or with one's ideals. But this does prevent the bodily changes wrought by sympathetic nervous stimulation, adrenalin has been released; overt action may be inhibited, but some of the effects of the emotion and nervous excitement are held over. Thus pent-up emotional disturbances may produce prolonged disorder in the bodily processes; at least making a person more subject to disease, if not actually causing the disease.

Of course, not all emotions are as violent as fear, anger, rage; and there are degrees of fear and anger. The reactions of the nervous system are not all equally intense; in mild emotions there will be only slight circulatory, digestive, respiratory, and hormone dysfunction. And when the emotion is prolonged, the effects are prolonged; serious consequences of chronic emotions are made evident by the great number who are made sick, in a great variety of forms—the whole range of psychosomatic ills. Anxiety and worry are chronic fears, with chronic effects on the whole body. Jealousy, envy, resentments, grudges, hostile feelings, are all chronic anger. There are also emotions that we can poorly define, mixed feelings, such as frustration, dejection, depression, unhappiness, and a desire to escape from hard situations or responsibilities. Feelings of guilt, especially when repressed, and other less defined emotions, all have their influence on the nerves and, through them, on the whole body and its organs. This will be more than amply demonstrated by the reports of sick folk in medical literature for any who care to investigate.

The parasympathetics in many ways have an effect contrary to that of the sympathetics: they slow the action of the heart instead of stimulating it; they stimulate secretion of the digestive juices and promote movements of the stomach and intestines; they maintain moderate contraction of the bronchial tubes, and if over-stimulated cause them to constrict and impede breathing, as in asthma. In general, the action of the parasympathetics is conservative, promoting the assimilation of nutriment; the sympathetics promote the consumption and use of nutriment, the spending of energy. Normally there is a balance between these two parts of the nervous system; together in harmony they maintain a fairly stable equilibrium of the complex processes and functions of the body. Emotions throw this balance out of order, and health is impaired and actual disease may follow.

PATHOLOGY OF THE EMOTIONS

The effects of emotions on the digestive system are probably the best-known of the psychosomatic aspects of illness or dysfunction. Everyone who has had to speak or sing in public knows how emotion can stimulate the sympathetic system, inhibit the secretion of saliva and make his mouth dry. Pleasurable anticipation of food, or food odors, stimulates the parasympathetics, and an abundance of saliva is secreted; but if the odors or associations are disagreeable, there will not be this salivary secretion. In the same way, gastric secretion is affected by emotions. This was demonstrated by the great physiologist, Pavlov, in his studies on dogs; but it was shown a long time before by the American doctor, Beaumont: he treated a man who had an abdominal wound, and it healed, leaving an opening into the stomach through which Dr. Beaumont could look directly and observe the condition of the stomach under various conditions. He found that pleasure and good feeling promoted digestion, that anger or anxiety decreased the secretion of gastric juice, and that food might lie in the stomach a long time undigested. Other physiologists have seen the stomach lining get red and inflamed, and even ulcerous, under the continued influence of strong emotions.

Cannon tells of a woman who came to Boston for examination in a clinic: she was given a test breakfast, and when the stomach contents were analyzed practically no gastric juice was found, and the food from the night before was undigested. It appeared that her husband had taken advantage of her trip to the city to get drunk, and had given her a miserable time; her stomach refused to do its work. They tried again, and after a good rest and good behavior on the part of her husband the stomach test was normal. (There is a lesson in this for parents as to feeding children, and for us all: make the meal time a pleasant time.) All of us have experienced digestive upsets after emotional disturbances.

More recently another man with an opening into the stom-

ach has been studied.[8] The man worked in the laboratories
for a good many years with Dr. Wolff. He was observed almost every day for years, and the doctors learned to tell the
state of his emotions by the appearance of his stomach lining. Once when some papers for which he was responsible
were misplaced, his face got pale and the mucosa of his stomach
grew paler by the minute, as he feared loss of his job. When
the papers were found, his stomach began to regain its normal
pink color. This was a typical fear reaction. On another day
he was reprimanded for his failure to keep the apartment
clean: he grew red in the face, but he dared not express his
anger at the rebuke, and he was boiling mad; the gastric mucosa
was red, the gastric acid was much increased and motility was
increased. After his sustained resentment, the doctors found
small hemorrhages on the surface of the stomach lining.

Emotions often cause vomiting. Alvarez tells of a young
woman who received a menacing letter from the customs col-
lector; she was so frightened that she took to her bed and
vomited day and night for a week. She was cured when the
doctor took the note and went to the Custom House, paid
$3.85 for her and presented her with the receipted bill.[9] Some
people have diarrhoea under emotional stress; others may be
constipated.

The relation of emotions to "ulcers of the stomach" is too
well established to be seriously questioned. One of our leading
physiologists says that he does not hope to produce the human
type of ulcers in dogs until he can get them to worrying about
the stock market—or something else. Alvarez quotes a patient:

[8] "Life Situation, Emotions and Disease," in *Teaching Psychotherapeutic
Medicine*, pp. 380 f., edited by Helen L. Witmer (Commonwealth Fund,
New York, 1947).

[9] Walter C. Alvarez, *Nervousness, Indigestion, and Pain*, p. 8 (Paul B.
Hoeber, New York, copyright, 1943).

"All my troubles must be psychic in origin, because my first attack came twenty-five years ago when my girl refused to marry me; the second came later when she changed her mind and I had the excitement of a big wedding; the third came when, in the crash of 1907, I got caught with all my money tied up in a copper mine; the fourth came in 1918 with the strain of my participation in the Argonne drive; the fifth came in 1929 when I lost all my savings." [10]

There may be a great variety of digestive disorders in emotional states: such as discomfort in swallowing, or swallowing air and belching it up again; heartburn, bloating, or quivering sensations in the abdomen, are common; nervous indigestion is well known; "biliousness" may be only emotional disturbance of bile elimination, resulting in poor digestion of fats. The colon is often involved in emotional disturbances: constipation or diarrhoea may be emotional in origin; "colitis" is often aggravated, if not produced, by psychic ills.

The sick person generally does not recognize the underlying emotional cause; the more serious psychosomatic illnesses have an unrecognized, suppressed or repressed emotional factor. This is well illustrated by a patient of mine years ago: he was a Korean preacher, suffering from chronic indigestion, loss of weight, and generally bad condition; he was truly ill. It was brought out by my colleague psychiatrist that the real cause of his sickness was unhappiness—to put it mildly—in his relations with his wife: she was a woman who wanted the comforts of life and some of its pleasures, but his salary as a poor preacher in poor Korea could not meet her wants, and she was making life miserable for him, and he for her. He was shown how his resentment was destroying his home and his health; being a real Christian man, he went home and achieved understanding and

[10] *Ibid.*, p. 17.

sympathy with his wife. When I next saw him he was a much changed man; his illness was gone; he looked in good health and happy.

The adverse effects of emotions on digestion are thus well known: but I want to point out also that pleasant emotions have a favorable effect. It is more than the absence of disturbing emotions: happiness, joy, and peace of mind promote good digestion, through their effects on the parasympathetic nerves inducing secretion of the digestive juices and normal movements of the alimentary canal. "A merry heart doeth good like a medicine." [11] But it does not pay to get too excited in even a joyous way: the excitement may upset the nervous balance that controls the system. One who is really enjoying life will probably have a good digestion.

None of us needs to be told that excitement will make the heart beat fast; and even the excitement of going to a doctor will bring about an increase of blood pressure—doctors make allowance for that, especially on the patient's first visit. But I think that if a patient has nervous instability that allows his blood pressure to go up in this way, it is probable that later he will have high blood pressure. It is a common and quite well-substantiated idea that the tension and strenuousity of life make for high blood pressure. Many victims of this trouble have learned that they must not give way to temper, or they will suffer for it. Common stories are told of people who have burst a blood vessel and died in a fit of anger. Alvarez tells of an elderly man, a choleric millionaire, whose blood pressure would go up from around 170 to 230 or so, every time he flew into a tantrum of rage; he was so frightened by this that he promised to control himself. But one day he grew angry at a man who tried to cheat him in a deal. He was overheard to

[11] Proverbs 17:22.

say: "Quick! Get out of here. I can't afford to get mad at you."
Some of his expressions are not for polite society but he had
learned the lesson that emotion does affect blood pressure.[12]

Wolff found that emotions change the circulation not only
in the stomach: emotional stress may cause the blood vessels
in the nose to dilate; and under other conditions there may be
pallor and swelling. The circulation and temperature of the
skin are changed by emotions. Wolff tells of a professor who
was to give a lecture and was uncertain as to the reception
he might expect from the audience; his anxiety increased his
before- and after-exercise pulse rates, blood pressure, and
heart output. He was disappointed in the arrangements for
his lecture, and the audience was not capable of appreciating
his contribution; he felt he had wasted his time, and was
humiliated and angry. It took several days for him to get back
to normal pulse and blood pressure.[13]

After World War I, there was much talk of "soldier's heart."
There were no definite organic findings, but men were truly
incapacitated with cardiac symptoms under the stress of hardships and strain and fear—often unrecognized fear. This was
not just an affliction of soldiers; many people in ordinary life
have the same distressing symptoms; so it was called "neuro-
circulatory asthenia," or some other unobjectionable term.
Doctors now speak of cardiac neuroses. All of this shows how
the heart and circulatory system are subject to emotional influences.

All of us have experienced changes in respiration under emotional stress: the increased and even labored breathing of anger
and frustrations and conflicts is well known; the frequent sigh-
ing of depression is often seen. It may be doubted that there is

[12] Alvarez, *op. cit.*, p. 448.
[13] Wolff, *op. cit.*, pp. 388 f.

asthma of purely psychic origin, but it is undeniable that many cases do have large emotional factors. Bronchioles that are sensitized by allergy may react with over-contraction under the ordinary stimulus of emotions by way of the autonomic nerves. Medical literature gives many instances of this.

Not only are the involuntary muscles of the digestive system, the heart, the blood vessels, the bronchial tubes, and other internal organs, affected by emotions; the muscles of the skeletal system, the voluntary muscles, also may react to emotional strain: the muscles of the back and neck may become over-contracted and stay so, causing pain in the back of the head and neck, and along the spine. Doctors are now even talking about "psychogenic rheumatism," and believe that some cases of arthritis belong in this psychic group. Tremors are common in emotional stress; patients who have had a paralysis and become spastic may be worse when excited; Parkinson's disease —"shaking palsy"—may at first be noticed only during emotional upsets.

And recently the dermatologists, "skin doctors," have been saying a good deal about "neurodermatitis"; in many cases the psychic disturbance makes the eczema and other skin diseases much worse; some are thought to be entirely psychogenic.

Our common speech has many expressions of this bodily effect of emotions: people get "red in the face," "hot under the collar," "pale with fright"; fear brings a "cold sweat"; some things "take one's breath away"; we get a "lump in the throat" or something "turns the stomach"; we feel our heart "jump"; we may have "cold feet"; and often we "sigh heavily." We do not take all these expressions literally; but they do indicate common knowledge and experience of the effects of emotions on the body; and these things have been known long enough to become common expressions in our language. There seems to be good support for the idea that emotions express themselves in an "organ language." Nausea and vomiting may come from something in his life situation that the patient "cannot stomach"; or he may be trying to rid himself of guilt. Vomiting in small children often means rebellion against coercion to eat certain foods—or any food; sometimes they will have no nausea at nursery school, but other meals at home will not be retained. Heart troubles may come from an unsatisfied need for love and appreciation; "heart attacks" may be anxiety attacks. Loss of appetite may come from lack of satisfaction in life, from being emotionally starved. Fatigue often means that emotional conflicts have used up so much energy there is little left for anything else. Muscle tension is often the sign of emotional tension, and the tense muscles give rise to many aches and pains. Weiss and English suggest that it would be better many times to give up trying to find a "focal infection" and pay attention to "focal conflict" [14]—the emotional conflict that may be only half conscious or even subconscious. Itching and dermatoses may be due to scratching one's self, martyr-like, instead of scratching someone else as we would like to do.

One other point needs to be brought out in this discussion of the pathology of emotions: the symptoms in psychosomatic disease are often related to, if not actually due to, repressed childhood emotional experiences. Dunbar calls these "delayed-action mines of childhood." [15] Very real emotional conflicts can come from these long-repressed childhood experiences; such as re-

[14] Weiss and English, *op. cit.*, p. 10.
[15] Flanders Dunbar, *Mind and Body: Psychosomatic Medicine*, p. 17 (Random House, New York, 1947).

pressed resentment toward parents because of real or imagined harshness or injustice. Because of guilt in feeling thus toward a parent the child represses the hostile feeling; but in later life it may be a factor in his psychosomatic illness, as he meets the hardships of life and struggles for recognition and honor and security.

II

Emotions and Sickness

PSYCHOGENIC FACTORS OF ILLNESS

Mixed emotions are involved in nearly all psychosomatic illnesses. But there is practically always some form of anxiety underlying the sickness and some form of conflict involved. The conflict may be the cause of the anxiety; and in cases where the dominant emotion is hate or guilt, anxiety is also involved; and there is conflict. Conflict seems to be present in all cases of psychogenic illness: conflicts between desires that tend in opposite ways, as when we want to do the proper thing but something urges us to the selfish thing; conflicts between instinctual urges, or neurotic trends that are contrary; or it may be because one cannot, or dare not, give expression to what his instincts and emotions urge on him. A child may resent his parent's discipline, and get into a conflict between this emotion and the feeling of love for his parent or fear of the consequences of giving way to his anger; these conflicts often result in guilt as well as in anxiety.

Freud emphasized the idea that conflict between instincts, desires, or drives, and the situation in which one finds himself, leads to illness; and that frustration or denial of the normal expression of the instincts leads to inner conflicts and to development of symptoms as ways of meeting the life situation. He emphasized the danger of repressing these instinctual desires. He put his greatest emphasis on the "libido": in this he includes much that is not generally considered to be "sex," the urge to life as a whole. We may consider it unfortunate that he chose the word "libido" because of its connotations of unrestrained sex; yet it is undeniable that sex is a major factor in many inner conflicts of neuroses—he makes it *the* factor.

Adler does not emphasize the libido, but assumes a drive or urge to mastery, to superiority; failure or frustration in this urge results in a feeling of inferiority, anxiety, and conflicts. Jung, like Freud and Adler, emphasizes the unconscious urges or instincts, and the conflicts between them and the more conscious desires and purposes. All psychologists and psychiatrists who have to do with sick or maladjusted people recognize the importance of the unconscious, and of conflicts; though they are far from Freud in his insistence on the primacy of sexual factors. Horney may be cited as an example of modern psychoanalysts: she says, "In the center of psychic disturbances are unconscious strivings developed in order to cope with life despite fears, helplessness, and isolation. I have called them 'neurotic trends.' " [1] Most of the neurotic trends are natural and normal impulses, but in neuroses they are exaggerated and impulsive: e.g., a desire for affection and approval is quite normal; but it may become obsessive, so that a person must have approval from everybody or be made miserable.

I do not think one needs to go along with the psychoanalysts, even when they have given up much of Freud! Most people do not need the "depth psychology" that psychoanalysis assumes necessary: a more simple and common sense understanding is possible in most cases, and a more eclectic psychology will help most of us.

I made a study of several hundred case reports of psycho-

[1] Karen Horney, *Self-Analysis*, p. 40 (W. W. Norton & Co., New York, 1942).

somatic illnesses, and found that one could very seldom pick out one single emotion as the cause of the sickness. Anxiety was the most common emotion; and in some degree it seems to be involved in most cases. It was found associated with resentment and hate, and guilt complicates these, while sex maladjustments may also add troubles. Sex is more likely to be a cause of anxiety or hate or guilt-feeling than of itself to cause the illness. Symptoms in many cases are escape mechanisms; but in other cases the sickness seems to be itself the result of visceral changes wrought by the autonomic nervous system, not an escape; it seems to be directly a result of the emotional disturbance.

Anxiety is chronic fear, and it may take many forms and arise out of many situations; it may arise from quite conscious fears, or from those completely unconscious or repressed. The feeling of insecurity in a child who believes himself unloved or displaced, of a wife or husband who fears losing the beloved, of one who is not secure in his living or employment or support—such are very common anxieties in the ill. The anxiety of a person who feels inadequate to his responsibilities; the unconfessed but haunting dread of some illness, such as cancer, heart disease, tuberculosis, or the fear of death; anxiety over a loved one who is ill or in danger or lost—these are common factors in psychosomatic sickness. And sexual anxieties are common in both sexes.

Hate and *resentment* are chronic *anger*; jealousy is anger and fear. These emotions present a great variety of forms, conscious and unconscious: it may be hostility toward parents for lack of love and appreciation, for harsh or cruel treatment, for injustices, for domineering, for too great possessiveness thwarting the child's desire for self-expression and independence. It may be toward brothers or sisters, toward husband or wife, toward business associates or employers, toward teachers, toward government authorities, or toward persons in a social way; but the closer the association, the greater the dependence, the greater the conflict.

Guilt and *shame* are very commonly associated with anxiety or hate and resentment. The guilt may come from many causes: it is frequently due to disobeying parents, along with hostility, and because of the hate; it often comes from secret or overt sex sins, or from youthful or marital infidelity; it comes from wrongs done and crimes committed—including mistakes, sometimes where the conscience is over-sensitive and good judgment would not condemn the thing done; and not infrequently it comes from the sense of sin before God.

In some cases the psychic factor is a longing to escape from an unpleasant situation or duty; in others the symptoms seem to be means to gain or hold attention and love, or to dominate another, to get one's own way, or to keep a child "tied to mother's apron strings." Grief and sorrow appear to be the dominant factors in some cases.

It may be anticipating what I hope to discuss more fully later, but I call attention here to the fact that this account of the emotions that tend to psychosomatic illness, indicates the place that religion should have in their cure and prevention. Religion has to do with anxiety, worry, fear of all kinds, with anger, hate and resentment, jealousy, envy, and with guilt and sorrow.

COMMON PSYCHOSOMATIC ILLS

The great majority of these ills require no "depth psychology" or prolonged psychoanalysis; they are relatively on the surface, though not fully conscious as causes of the ills.

They may be cleared up by study enough to gain insight, especially with the help of a wise counsellor. It is not necessary that everyone go to a psychiatrist or professional consulting psychologist: many physicians are now helping these patients; and ministers are doing much to help people along these lines; while some people can help themselves with self-study. But one should caution anyone attempting self-analysis to be sure he does not have some organic physical disease—the same applies to counsellors, who should find out if there is a physical basis for the disease before treating the psychic symptoms. Let me cite some illustrative case reports:

While writing this, I saw a woman in my clinic and took her history: she was the mother of six children, and having a hard time financially. I asked her about headaches, and she quickly replied, "Yes, I have headaches whenever I get mad." Many other people find that they get headaches when annoyed or angry, though they may not be as willing to admit the cause as that mother.

Horney tells of a man who came to realize the cause of his headaches while attending a musical comedy with his wife and some friends. He felt well when they left home, and during the show his head began to ache. At first he blamed it on the show, which was not as good as "the one he would have preferred;" then he realized that he resented being overruled in the choice of plays. A few days later he had another headache at a meeting of his business staff when things had not gone as he desired.[2] On subsequent occasions he searched for the hidden anger as soon as his headaches started, and he quit having headaches. Of course there are numerous other causes of headaches; but many are due to emotional conflicts.

[2] *Ibid.*, pp. 155 ff.

Migraine, or "sick headache," or "bilious headache," is very often the result of emotional tension. One of my former patients, widowed mother of a grown daughter, had migraine almost every time she unsuccessfully attempted to dominate her daughter. She admitted that there was some relation between her headaches and the difficulties she had with her daughter; but she did nothing to achieve right relations with the daughter as long as I knew her. The victims of migraine are usually intelligent, sensitive, tense people, easily upset and irritated; they are usually poorly adjusted to life, "in a hurry," and often "perfectionists."

Difficult life situations often result in emotional disturbances that make people ill. It took no psychiatry to find out what was the psychic trouble in another of my patients: she was a woman in her sixties, suffering from severe digestive difficulties, extreme fatigue, and many pains; she was on the verge of a breakdown, but was bravely trying to carry on; her husband was practically bedfast with a serious heart disease, their savings were gone, they had only one poor room to live in, eat in, and sleep in; and she was trying to work when she could get a chance. She had justifiable reasons for anxiety and worry, and the worry and anxiety took toll of her strength and health.

Ulcers of the stomach or duodenum are commonly affected by emotional stress, and hemorrhages may occur after financial reverses. Alvarez tells of an inventor who endured years of hard work and poverty. After his machine was installed by a big company and royalties were coming his way there was a change in the raw material and the machine clogged up. The company threatened to throw his machine out. He had a large hemorrhage from his ulcer, but directed changes in the machine from his bed; the difficulty was overcome and money again flowed in. But in three years the machine had to be fixed up six times, and he had six hemorrhages.[3]

Every doctor, consulting psychologist, minister, and social worker knows of many cases of illness due to, or aggravated by, marital unhappiness—and it is not always the woman who gets sick. I have patients with ulcers that are made worse by frivolous, selfish wives. But more often it is the wife who suffers. I see many women who have borne children to a man toward whom they now feel only hostility and resentment; they have many complaints and many symptoms. Often they are in truly poor health; but they feel unable to go away from the man. They are sick of ills that medicines or surgery cannot reach. Other women, generally younger, have separated from husbands and come to me with complaints of many ills; they are frustrated, disappointed, and with a guilty feeling. A woman came to Dr. Alvarez complaining of the pain of ulcers, loss of weight, severe headaches, and generally poor health. She was a happy, healthy woman three years earlier when she had married a handsome but quite stupid man; within a week she was desperately unhappy and soon was crazy to leave him. Then she realized that she was pregnant and dared not leave, for she was sick and would soon have a child to care for. She had no parents to go back to, and he had so little income he could not give her any support for separate maintenance. Her feeling was well summed up in one sentence: "We haven't enough money so I can even have a separate bed." [4] It takes no psychoanalysis to know the psychogenic origin of her illness; she really knew it, but could not, or would not, do what alone would remedy it.

[3] Walter C. Alvarez, *Nervousness, Indigestion, and Pain,* p. 17 (Paul B. Hoeber, Inc., New York).
[4] *Ibid.,* p. 275.

Other family relationships may be factors in illness. Ross gives a good illustration. A woman of about forty came to him complaining of extreme fatigue which she had had for four years; she had had rest-cures and had seemed to recover fully each time; but as soon as she went home, her symptoms recurred as badly as ever. She was asked about her home life: she confessed that she and her mother lived an impossible life together, full of bitterness and disagreements. Ross thinks the mother was probably "certifiable," an impossible woman. But when the younger woman faced up to the situation and realized that this was the cause of her sickness, she made the necessary adjustments in her own life and attitudes. When she went home this time there was no recurrence of her troubles, she got along peaceably for four years until the death of her mother; she had none of the old incapacitating fatigue and debilitating emotions.[5]

One could go on indefinitely adding more illustrations of the many illnesses brought on by common, easily recognized emotional states: anxiety over impending loss of a beloved one, or of one's own marriage going on the rocks; anxiety as to job and security; hostility toward the boss for some real or imagined grievance; unhappiness in life situation and work; fear of some disease, such as cancer, heart disease, or tuberculosis; the anxieties of the lonely, the homeless, the disabled and handicapped, those approaching old age and enfeeblement. Some of these will be illustrated in case studies given later.

ILLNESS AS AN ESCAPE

People do not deliberately get sick, or have an injury; but they may unconsciously use illness as a way of meeting a hard

---

[5] T. A. Ross, *The Common Neuroses*, p. 42 (permission Edward Arnold & Co., London—Williams Wilkins Co., American agents).

situation, and as a means of avoiding what seems a greater evil. They have an emotional need for sickness, to provide an alibi for not doing what they do not want to do, a way of escape from difficulties. The illness becomes what Dunbar calls "the beloved symptom," cherished because it affords some relief from the more dreaded alternative. Sometimes not even an operation is feared enough to make these patients give up their beloved symptoms. Sadler says: "When a timid soul engages in a flight from reality—when a person seeks to escape from the unbearable responsibilities of modern life—he most frequently decides (unconsciously) upon some type of digestive disorder as the most acceptable form of 'liberating illness.' All such 'escapists' are willing to undergo all sorts of surgical operations. They are many times 'all scarred up' like World War veterans. But surgeons are becoming educated. They are discovering that they cannot cut a pain out of the belly when that pain has an emotional origin. . . . Surgical operations do not cure either anxiety neuroses or periodic emotional depressions." [6]

Not all headaches used as excuses are unreal "polite fictions"; they are often very real, furnishing a good alibi; they may come from some emotional conflict below the level of consciousness. And of course we realize that not all headaches are emotional excuses. Of the same nature as the "alibi" headaches are the "diplomatic colds" that afflict some prominent—and not so prominent—folk. Gladstone's political opponents used to say that he had colds at "most convenient moments," when he could avoid having to attend meetings where he would have to face some embarrassing questions; and they noted that he would be his usual robust self the next day. He was not the only one to use such escapes.

[6] William S. Sadler, *Modern Psychiatry*, p. 10 (C. V. Mosby Co., St. Louis).

It was not cowardice that disabled the victims of "shell shock" among soldiers exposed to prolonged dangerous duty; but it did provide a way out of the situation. "Shell shock" was not often mentioned in World War II; but many thousands of physically strong young men were incapacitated for military service by "neuropsychiatric disorders" in the recent war. The disability was real, even though the victims were not conscious of the fear and desire for escape that led them into it— they were not malingerers, though they did flee into illness. Many are the conditions in our strenuous, selfish, modern life that may lead to psychosomatic illness.

As to the reality of these illnesses, I wish to quote again from Sadler: "Psychoneurotic pain is not imaginary; it is as real and distressing to the patient as 'organic' pain, and the accompanying fear and anxiety make it worse. Since emotional maladjustment is the basis of such fear and anxiety as well as the symptom itself, these reactions are more intense than those based on a bona fide organic difficulty." [7]

A young man of a prominent family in South America won a scholarship to a university in the United States; he was given a most enthusiastic send-off and honors. But before his first year was out, he was at the office of Dr. Alvarez complaining of indigestion, a vague "misery" in his abdomen, and inability to work. It turned out that "coeds," movies, and night clubs had been given more time and energy than his studies, and he "flunked." The doctor points out that it would look much better for him to go back home as an unfortunate invalid than as a failure. [8]

Elizabeth Barrett is an almost classical example of a young

[7] *Ibid.*, p. 2.
[8] Alvarez, *op. cit.*, p. 278.

woman invalid who made sickness an escape. She was the eld-
est of eleven children fathered by a domestic tyrant, brought
into the world by a frail and harassed mother, who died soon
after the youngest was born. At fifteen Elizabeth fell from a
pony and injured her spine; she made a good recovery from
that—but she was an invalid for twenty years: she escaped
some of the paternal rages by being ill; she got care and thought-
ful attention in her illness; she was given a room to herself in
spite of the number of children in the home; and though she
did suffer, there were compensations: she had privacy for her
reading and writing; she had selected visitors; then when her
poetry and other writings won for her a literary reputation, the
family gave her even more attention—but not love. Her dramatic cure after she was nearly forty years of age, confirms
the psychic nature of her illness: married and taken away from
her unhappy home, and given the rich love of Robert Brown-
ing, she was soon able to climb mountains; and at forty-three
she bore a healthy son. She remained in good health, for, as
Dunbar says, "She didn't need her symptoms any longer." [9]

A hundred years ago hysteria was a very common illness
among young women; they generally acquired the trouble at
the age when sexual passions were developing and were denied
expression; or in later life when the sexual satisfactions were
impossible. The inner conflict led to symptoms, and hysterical
fits were quite common; the inner unrest and unhappiness were
converted into physical symptoms. "Most nervous patients experience a 'transfer' of their emotional tension and suppres-
sion to some internal organ. This produces the distressing
visceral symptoms—the neurotic 'organ recitals'—from which

[9] Flanders Dunbar, *Mind and Body: Psychosomatic Medicine*, p. 32 (Random House, New York).

so many of these poorly integrated personalities suffer" (Sadler [10]). I will only refer to the case of Mary Baker Eddy, and her hysterical fits—more about them later. But Dunbar well points out that hysterical fits are not now considered respectable for nice girls or women.

In my medical college days, I was much impressed by the case of a girl in a family I knew quite well: she was in her teens, and for months had been unable to eat a normal meal without throwing it up in a short time; of course she was very thin and pale and weak. Finally she was brought to the city for more expert study and treatment. The doctor in charge called for consultation and for laboratory work. It was found that she had a special type of anemia, common then but rare now, "chlorosis"; the consultant said that he had never seen a patient with that form of anemia who was not a liar. This greatly shocked everyone; for the girl was of a religious family, and was herself very pious. The doctor insisted that no girl could live as long as she had without eating more than she was known to eat—even allowing for the cocoa butter that was rubbed on her abdomen. It was finally agreed to mark and number every bit of food left on the table, and set a watch over it; what was the consternation of the family to find that the girl got up in the night and ate a hearty meal from the table, went back to bed and slept soundly till morning. She was hysterical when confronted with the knowledge of her deceit; but she gave up vomiting her meals. I did not find out what was the emotional conflict that made this young girl undergo months of hunger and the distress of vomiting the food she ate when people knew about it. But the exposure of her hysteria did not cure her permanently; she lived only a relatively short time, but I do not know what caused her death.

[10] *Op. cit.*, p. 3.

ILLNESS AS A MEANS

Very closely related to those cases where the patient uses illness as an escape, are those which are used as a means to secure love and attention or to hold dominion over some other person. It may be a mother who develops symptoms to keep her child tied to her apron strings; or it may be a seeking on the child's part to get again the tenderness and care that its mother gave in childhood. The "beloved symptom" is used to gain sympathy and to evade responsibility: it is reversion to childhood, or refusal to grow up, a neurotic trend to dependence or dominance—of course, not consciously. Let me cite a few illustrations:

A mother and daughter went two thousand miles to a clinic for treatment of the mother's abdominal pain. She had been in good health until a few months before: the doctor found that her sickness began soon after her two daughters left home and rented an apartment on their own. The girls had done this because they could never entertain boy-friends at home; the mother would quiz any visitor about his financial prospects and his intentions, and the young man would not return. So the girls decided to get away from all that. But when they left, the parents were deprived of the financial support the daughters had given them; the husband and father was much of a ne'er-do-well, and the mother was anxious about the money as well as desirous of keeping her girls with her. It was not that she intended to be hard on the girls or their friends, but she made herself sick to hold them.[11]

Recently I read in a medical journal the story of a woman who had asthma for ten years; it was clearly shown to be psycho-

[11] Alvarez, *op. cit.*, p. 280.

somatic: the first attacks came on soon after her marriage to an irritable, hyperthyroid husband who wanted himself to be the one to receive attentions. She had nasal operations, and allergy treatments—but to no avail. Her husband became interested in another woman, and was very intolerant of her complaints; he urged her to divorce him, but she was not willing to give him freedom while she suffered so much. He moved his mistress into an apartment nearby; she knew it because she had had detectives follow him. It was noted that her attacks came on every day at the same time. In spite of treatment she got no relief, even from adrenalin injections. Finally she went to Vichy, France; while there she had no asthma; she was able to do almost anything she wished, and eat anything; she was jolly and optimistic. But when she went back home, she was well until 7 P.M., the time of her usual attacks, and then she had a bad one. The asthma continued as before until she went to Arizona and then she was free of it for three months. Once again when she got home, promptly at 7 P.M. the asthma started again. Finally she left her husband, and later secured a divorce; she then had no use for adrenalin or asthma treatments; she was having no asthma. After two years she became engaged to be married again; she was free of asthma till two days before the wedding. She went to her doctor and was reassured again, though she remained a little dubious; she had a little trouble with asthma for a couple of days, then remained free from it. However, when they had to move in with the mother of her husband and she saw his concern over his mother, the asthmatic attacks came on again; but they cleared up after the death of his mother when her husband turned his affections to her again; she has had no more asthma. Clearly this was a case where a woman's asthma was in part due to her emotional conflict and her longing for love, and it was used to try to hold her husband—not deliberately, but unconsciously.[12]

Children who are lonely, feeling a need for their mother's love and attention, or jealous of a sibling, often develop symptoms of illness as a means to hold or to win back the love of their mother. Of course, it may be to gain the affection of others besides the mother. And it may be that illness is avoided in childhood, but that in later life, when confronted by a similar situation, sickness may develop. These are what Dunbar called "delayed-action mines of childhood." Many of these will not require any deep analysis, but some will be more concealed and obscure, repressed.

It is easy to see that Mary Baker Eddy used illness as a means to dominate her family, and to gain her own way. She was a nervous, frail girl, over-sensitive to noises, and a harsh word was positively painful to her; she could not go to school because the children were too noisy; so she was allowed to stay at home. At home she was always "showing off" and "putting on airs"; and when she failed to get the attention she desired, in her frustration, her nerves got worse than ever; she would get very excited and often have convulsive seizures; she had paroxysms of anxiety, and hallucinations were common. The family doctor said it was not epilepsy, and when pressed for a further statement, he said it was "hysteria mingled with a bad temper." But she never had to work at the household tasks like her brothers and sisters; they waited on her, while she read stories and dreamed of "something higher" as her destiny. Whenever she was crossed, she would have tantrums, "throw a fit," and thus she had her way; she dominated the household by her hysteria. In later life, she was inflexible in her

---

[12] J. A. Haiman, "Psychosomatic Approach to Treatment of Allergies, Bronchial Asthma, and Systemic Disorders," *Medical Record*, Vol. 161, pp. 467–473 (Sept., 1948).

iron-willed dominance over all who would submit, even having hysterical fits after she set up as a "moral healer." She disrupted the homes that received her; she remained a contradictory person—iron-willed, able to inspire others to belief and health; but she herself remained frail, weak, neurasthenic, and even convulsive. For the most part she kept aloof, but on occasion she would rally her will to go out and greatly impress people. In her later life, when she was the revered teacher of Christian Science, she did not need to have tantrums and throw hysterical fits to get her way: her word was law so long as she lived.[13]

I have discussed the emotions and how they may be a cause of sickness at this length not with the idea of telling anyone how to be a psychiatrist or consulting psychologist or counsellor, but with the aim of helping common people to understand how these things can be, and with this insight to help themselves and others to better health. I also believe that these facts show how religion can be a means of helping ourselves and others in meeting the conflicts in our own inner lives, for anxieties, fears, hostilities, and resentments are just the kind of thing with which wholesome religion can deal better than any other method of healing or prevention.

THE SUBCONSCIOUS

We have many times referred to the subconscious, or unconscious, in our discussion; and it seems that a brief consideration of this phase of the psyche should help us to understand ourselves better and to know how to help others more effectively. Of course, this is not comprehensive.

Psychology is the science of the mind, the psyche, as a

[13] Data largely from Stefan Zweig, *Mental Healers* (Viking Press, New York).

whole; yet most textbooks on the subject are devoted mainly to the conscious psyche. But there is a vast store below the levels of consciousness, the "subconscious" or "unconscious." The psyche is sometimes compared to an iceberg, only a small part of which is above the surface of the ocean; the vast bulk lies below, unseen. What a chaotic condition our minds would be in if all our memories of experiences, our instincts and urges, our ideals and goals, all our psyche were conscious all the time!

Freud was the popularizer of the concept of the "unconscious." But before Freud's writings were published, my first psychology teacher, before 1900, introduced me to this phase of psychology: that in memory things are out of consciousness, but they may be recalled; that nothing is ever forgotten, and that, in theory at least, things may be recalled to consciousness. What is now in the conscious will become subconscious; and what is now unconscious may come to consciousness.

Freud proposed a three-fold psyche: "the conscious"—that of which we are aware; "the fore-conscious" or "pre-conscious"—the domain of memories that may be readily recalled; and the "unconscious" or "subconscious," the main bulk of the psyche. He postulated a "censor" standing at the door of consciousness to keep down unwelcome thoughts and emotions or urges. Ideas, memories of experiences, desires that are not acceptable to the "ego" are pushed down out of consciousness; this is repression; it avoids conflicts in the open, but does not do away with unconscious conflict. For the most part the instinctual drives and urges belong to the unconscious; but they may become conscious. Freud and his followers have postulated an organization of ideas or emotions, after their repression and their reappearance in disguised forms in consciousness, as complexes. Psychoanalysis attempts to trace and expose these disguises—to uncover the complexes.

Sadler says that we should "regard the unconscious as designating a group of mental activities which lack the quality of consciousness." It is "not merely a passive realm of engrams or memory patterns, but a very active domain of psychic life; *the subconscious is dynamic*, but its processes are only remotely related to reality. They are carried on with that same disregard of reality that is manifested in one's dream life." He goes on to say: "It is a great mistake to conceive of the subconscious as existing apart from ordinary personality consciousness. The academic psychologists are undoubtedly right when they insist that 'there is no such thing as the subconscious'; technically speaking, human consciousness is a unified experience, a single and continuous domain of feeling, thinking, willing, and acting. Nevertheless, from the practical or clinical standpoint we are compelled to admit that the mind is very definitely divided at any one moment into two distinct phases—the conscious and the unconscious—and this forces us to take the subconscious into account in discussing the diagnosis and treatment of the neuroses, the psychoses, and other phases of personality maladjustment." [14]

The subconscious is part of our psyche; it belongs to us personally: we have, or are, but one psyche. As in our daily lives we have many things stored away for use when wanted, but not kept in the living room; so what is in the subconscious may be brought into consciousness when needed. There may be delay in getting the memory to bring it out; but we all have had the experience of wanting to recall something that would not come on demand; we know we have known it; then later some association brings it back, or it comes like a flash back into memory. It is not an "ego" in conflict with an "id"

[14] Sadler, *op. cit.*, pp. 87, 89.

or a "libido": the psyche is one and acts as one. Conflicts are not between autonomous, or semi-autonomous parts of our psyche; it is not some instinct or urge, or libido fighting with the ego. It is "I" that have desires and impulses that are not harmonious: "I" want to be an honorable, upright man and hold the esteem of my fellows, while at the same time "I" would like the selfish gratification I might gain by some act I consider unworthy of my best self. The conflict may be in part below the conscious level, or it may be above it: one may be fully conscious of a desire to do full duty, and just as fully aware of a desire to be at ease and avoid the strain or danger in the line of duty. The subconscious, instinctual urge is often in conflict with the conscious ideal or desire: a child may hold deeply repressed resentment against a parent for harsh treatment or lack of love, and at the same time hold a feeling of duty toward parents—a conflict at the instinctual levels unrecognized by the child. Such ambivalence is common in neuroses.

Besides this which may be called the "personal unconscious," the growth of our psyche out of our own personal experiences, Jung has described a "collective unconscious," or "racial unconscious." This is the result of our inheritance; something of the racial experience and learning becomes ours. This is assumed to include our native instincts; and as such is unlearned but is ours from birth, inherited. Infants have little psyche besides this racial subconscious; their actions and reactions are instinctive and automatic; the subconscious is master. As we grow and develop, this dominance of the subconscious is reduced—not eliminated. Much of our emotional difficulty and illness are due to failure to outgrow this domination of the subconscious; and sometimes there is regression back to this infantile "tyranny of the subconscious."

Much is made of the conflicts that arise from the subconscious impulses, instincts, and urges with our "ego," our better self, our ideals and aims. Psychiatry seems at times to be a study of these conflicts, conscious and subconscious. Conflicts cannot be avoided. Sadler well says: "Conflict lies at the very basis of life. Just as certainly as this is true of the physical life, so it appears as a factor in the development of psychic life; therefore it is not strange that conflicts arise between the self-preservation urges and those higher ones of race preservation, as well as between other groups. If we regard as primitive instincts such impulses as self-assertion and self-abasement, we can do no less than recognize that such emotions are destined to be in comparatively continuous conflict." [15] But the conflicts can be resolved by an integration, or sublimation, in which a measure of satisfaction of both conflicting impulses is achieved, facing reality frankly.

This dynamic subconscious certainly brings plenty of problems and difficulties to each of us, and is the major factor in psychoneuroses and psychoses. But we must not think that it is all bad: there are healing, unifying, integrating elements like courage, faith, and love down in the very deepest depths of our being. The subconscious is more than a store of things good and bad; it is a power that can enrich us as well as plague us.

It is in the subconscious that most of the psychogenic factors of illness are to be found. And it is in the subconscious that religion does its most effective work for health, imparting faith and hope in place of fears and anxieties, inspiring to goodwill and love instead of hate and resentment, fixing the mind on the Lord rather than on the difficulties and disappointments and troubles of life. The subconscious is the realm of the work of the Holy Spirit.

[15] *Ibid.*, p. 92.

III

Faith Healing and the Cults

POWER OF THE MIND AT MISCHIEF has surely been well demonstrated: but the mind also has great power for health. Every doctor knows how much the will to live, the attitude of the patient, means in the cure of illness. Some people give up easily, and the most skillful medical care will not avail; while other patients survive in spite of the most severe sickness. Some patients are poor surgical risks because of the lack of will, or deep desire to live; others survive the most serious operations, for they do not give up, they positively will to live.

A story in *Reader's Digest*, February, 1949, well illustrates this power of the mind: it was the story of a wife whose husband devotedly loved her, but neglected to tell her. She had headaches; she was not happy. Then came an attack of appendicitis; she fainted in the car on the thirty-mile drive into town to the doctor. The appendix had ruptured, and she was in a desperate condition. The operation was performed and she rallied for a time; then she began to fail. The doctor found out from her that she felt her big, strong husband did not need her; when he told the husband something of this, the husband excused himself because he was not a talking man, but he vowed he would make her well by giving her his own blood. During the transfusion, he told her she had to get well for his sake, that he needed her, and loved her. When the doctor took the needle from her vein, he found that her feeble pulse, which had not responded to other blood transfusions, was now strong and steady. She did get well, and became strong and happy. But the doctor never told either of them that the husband's blood type was not suited to her, and that he had drawn the husband's blood into a bottle to use for someone else, and that what he had given her was from the blood bank. What that woman needed to make her live was assurance of love and appreciation. It was not the blood she received into her veins, but a new emotion, joy and love, that gave her a will to live and brought her back to health.

The power of suggestion is well known: all of us have experienced the effects of suggestion; we begin to feel less well or even really sick, when people remark that we do not look well. At times when we have been feeling below par, we get a real lift and feel much better when told that we are looking remarkably fine. Medical students suffer from the symptoms of diseases they are studying: as a doctor friend says, all his classmates suffered pains around the heart when they studied about angina pectoris and had to get electrocardiograms to reassure themselves. A generation ago Coué was famous for his suggestion, "Every day in every way I am getting better and better." There can be no reasonable doubt that suggestions of health do have an effect; and it is more than just the banishing of unhealthy thoughts and emotions; there is a positive health value in suggestions of health—witness the cures of faith healers, healings at shrines, and the healing cults. Healers make use of this power: impressive settings and fixtures influence the mind; they may use elaborate rituals, or simple but truly impressive rites—and what can be more suggestive than earnest prayers? Anointings and laying on of hands, with strong assurance in spoken words, are truly powerful suggestions; and their power is increased by mass suggestion when healings are publicly performed, as in a church or tabernacle.

This positive suggestion of health at least temporarily takes the mind of the sick person off his ills; it releases the autonomic nervous system from inimical influences; it sets healthy emotions in the place of those that led to illness. In cases where the symptoms are functional rather than based on organic disease, real cures may be effected. Some who have physical disease may temporarily be aroused to overcome the symptoms; they may get up and walk, leaving crutches behind, or gain enough strength to go on for a while apparently well. Some may have heart valves hopelessly damaged, or a coronary circulation inadequate, or a cancer that goes on destroying; the kidneys or liver may be irreparably diseased, or other conditions will in time take their life in spite of faith in the healer. They may go home to die of the same old disease, but some have a peaceful spirit and a different attitude in their illness, even helping others by their cheer and ministrations for a time. One might say in such cases that the *person* was cured even though his *body* was little helped. There is healing in "the expulsive power of a new affection."

But suggestion—and even with faith—is not all-powerful: there are many and tragic failures. There are no testimonials from the uncured; the failures do not get publicity. Where follow-up studies have been made, it is found that many of those who professed cures have died of their sickness within two years. Many are deluded into letting diseases that might be cured if adequately treated in time, just run their course. Some have had tragic endings, when under the new enthusiasm they have gone beyond the strength of weak hearts; ulcers or abscesses have ruptured, even in the excitement of a "healing." Yet there have been true cures.

NON-RELIGIOUS FAITH HEALING

Suggestion, faith, and expectancy have healing powers; even when the faith is not at all religious. Sir Humphrey Davy reported the cure of a paralytic in two weeks by the use of a thermometer: this was before clinical thermometers were in common use. Davy had an early-style thermometer and he used it on a visit to the sick man; the next day the patient asked for the thermometer again, saying that he had felt better right away after the "treatment" with it the day before. Giving him the thermometer to hold under his tongue every day enabled the paralyzed man to walk in two weeks. And just a short time ago, during a community X-ray survey in Los Angeles, a woman came a second time, saying that she had been helped so much by the former "treatment" that she wanted another— though it was but a chest X-ray picture.

The Rev. Dr. James M. Buckley was much interested in faith cures and hypnotism. He tells of taking a silver dollar wrapped in silk and, by using some mumbo-jumbo, curing toothaches. A great singer, a friend of Dr. Buckley, was taken violently ill with a headache and nausea just before a very important concert in New York City: two applications of the silver dollar to the singer's forehead cured the sickness and made a great success of the concert. On another occasion, he visited in the home of a woman suffering from inflammatory rheumatism; her hands were swollen, twisted, and helpless with the pain and contractures. After an impressive talk to the woman, he took some common steel knitting needles and held them above her hands; he told her not to think of her fingers but to fix her eyes on the points of the needles; the swollen, drawn fingers relaxed; the needles were slowly moved over her hands and all the pain left, except in one small spot. Dr. Buckley makes it clear that in these cases he made no appeal to religious faith; but he insists they were just as real as the cures of the healers, even though only temporary.[1] The knitting-needle cure would seem to have been hypnotic; and so do some of the practices of faith healers.

The power of hypnotism to allay and prevent pain is well shown by its use for anesthesia in operations: major operations have been performed with no other anesthesia; it is not an uncommon procedure with dentists. Recently I heard of a dentist who used hypnosis on his patients; and when he had to have a tooth extracted himself, he had another dentist hypnotize him and proceed with the extraction. But a root broke off and it was a more difficult job than he had expected; it began to hurt and he decided he had to have deeper hypnosis, so he used self-hypnosis for it and stopped the pain. I cannot help wondering if some of the reported results of a recent method of painless childbirth by teaching and training the expectant mother, may not be due to hypnosis, partially self-induced. I may add here, that hypnotism is not "putting to sleep"; it is rather a focusing of attention so that even pain does not cause a conscious reaction; it is an illustration of the power of suggestion, and may be used for healing.

Another instance of the power of non-religious faith and suggestion came under my observation while a medical student. I often noticed advertisements in the newspapers of Kansas City of an unscrupulous quack, "Dr. Carson, at Twelfth and Washington." A young newspaper man, who later became well known, George Creel, also saw them and thought they offered a fine chance for some clever parodies: so as a joke, he wrote some "ads" for "Good Old Dr. Arson, at Pelf and

[1] James M. Buckley, *Faith-Healing, Christian Science, and Kindred Phenomena*, pp. 22–23 (Century Co., New York, 1906).

Squashington"; they were published as satire. To the surprise of the writer, he immediately got responses from sick people and relatives of the sick who had been duped by the "Good Old Doctor." What began as a joke soon turned into a real crusade against quacks preying on the sick. The "Good Old Doctor" had an elaborate suite of offices fitted out to impress the neurotic sick; lights and shadows, curtains, tapestries, thick carpets, exotic fittings, all testified to the greatness of the "Good Old Doctor." He was impressive in looks and speech; when he laid his hands on the patient, the patient felt electric power enter his body—wires led to electric batteries and his hands completed the circuit; sometimes he had capsicum (red pepper) on his hands. The "Doctor" got so busy that he could not give time to laying on of hands and so he took to the use of small pieces of paper to which he had imparted his "magnetism." So all the patients had to do was to pay for the pieces of paper and fasten them to their underclothing, and they would get the "magnetism" of his hands. The "Good Old Doctor" had a great stock of abandoned crutches as evidence of his healing power. But Mr. Creel found out about his many failures and the tragedies he had wrought, though there were a few cures to his credit. After many years of reaping a golden harvest, "Good Old Doctor" was finally brought to trial, convicted, and fined five hundred dollars.

HEALINGS AT SHRINES

Miraculous cures by sacred relics and at shrines are reported from all lands and in all religions: we read of them in ancient Greece; they are reported from the Far East at temples and shrines; and we have them in the West in our own times. In primitive religions the priest is the medicine man; temples are places for prayers for healing. In Korea I saw prayers and incantations used in attempts to cure the sick; sacrifices and prayers for the sick were common in the temples there. We need not deny the reality of some cures by prayers at these shrines.

I have had no personal experience of visiting any of the famous shrines, such as that at Lourdes: I would like to repeat briefly some of the things Dr. Flanders Dunbar says about her visit to Lourdes:

The church is built above the grotto and spring where the Virgin Mary appeared; there are two uncomfortable stone buildings to house the sick. There is a daily schedule of activities: so many masses, so many hours of prayers for the sick at the baths and at the Stations of the Cross, and processions. The sick are taken at least once a day to the church, the baths, and to the procession of the Blessed Sacrament. Every variety of sickness is represented there. The common talk is of cures, of "miracles"; and the whole atmosphere is expectant. The patients bathe in the waters; they lie on the ramps in sunshine or rain, waiting their turn to receive the blessing of the priests, while pilgrims and onlookers shout prayers of the most moving sort.

At times patients who have not been able to get off a bed or stretcher for months, will get up and walk in processions; occasionally one will loudly claim to be cured, and a throng will gather about. But the attendants discourage demonstrations, to guard against hysteria; they emphasize the deep, quiet confidence of those really cured, in contrast to the hysterical excitement of others. One physician who had been directing pilgrimages to Lourdes for twelve years, told Dr. Dunbar that no patient of his had ever been cured; but he advised people to go there because many of them went away quiet and often remained quiet later. Another doctor said that the remarkable thing was the change in his patients, they got a different attitude toward their sickness; they became helpful to others—perhaps to the fretful patient in the next bed in the hospital. They had a different attitude toward their illness and were able to help others after they had gone back home to die —or to get well.

Dr. Dunbar was much interested in two girls she saw at Lourdes; both had advanced tuberculosis, and their doctors had advised against the trip, fearing they could not survive the journey. After the bath at the grotto, one of them shouted, "I am cured. Our Lady has cured me!" She was the center of much attention; but next day Dr. Dunbar saw her and she was much collapsed; the Sister was talking to her about discipline of the spirit. The other girl was quiet; she turned to her nurse and said, "I wonder if it can be true: I feel as if I were cured." She became a radiant personality; two days earlier she had been a sick girl on a stretcher, scarcely able to raise her hand, unable to eat, coughing painfully. Now she was radiant though emaciated, walking about, helping in the service of her companions; her cough disappeared, and she felt well. Three weeks later, Dr. Dunbar saw her in her home in a village near Como, Italy; she talked with the physician, who expressed his astonishment at the complete transformation of the girl. Dunbar concludes: "Seemingly miraculous cures occurred with and without faith; but a physician with a scientific understanding of the psychosomatic approach can effect cures by medical methods which would have been considered miracles a generation ago." [2]

[2] Condensed from Dunbar, *Mind and Body: Psychosomatic Medicine*, pp. 89–95 (Random House, New York, 1947).

CHRISTIAN SCIENCE

Outstanding among the healing cults is Christian Science; and it is in many ways a truly remarkable organization as to growth and influence. One has only to note the number of its churches in our cities to know that it has a great following; reading our daily papers, we see how it is kept before the public. We cannot know how many members the Christian Science church has: no figures as to membership have been given out since the U.S. Religious Census of 1936; and the by-laws of the church do not allow publication of figures. The total number of church organizations or societies is probably around 2,000; and 300,000 is a fair estimate of membership. This agrees with the Census figures. But I think it is fair to say that its influence is greater even than its numbers.

I am sure that reports of cures by Christian Science have been the greatest factor in its spread; but there are others that need to be mentioned.

Zweig in his book, *Mental Healers*,[3] calls attention to the cleverness of Mrs. Eddy in the choice of a name for her church: science was the great word of that day; and when she prefaced "Science" with the word "Christian," she had a term to conjure with. She flourished the name of the Christ, and appealed to the raising of Lazarus by Jesus as proof of her doctrine. The very name of "Christian Science" was enough to attract all the latent force of nebulous undenominational Christianity.

The emphasis on cures, on health and comfort, attracts people: everyone is interested in health and wants to avoid sickness and discomfort. There is a sound idea in this, for it is true that sick thoughts tend to make sick people, and healthy

[3] Chapter on Mary Baker Eddy, pp. 181 ff. (Viking Press, New York, 1932).

thoughts tend to good health. Too many people make themselves sick by worry and anxiety for any doctor to depreciate
this emphasis of the Christian Scientists—or of anyone else.
There is some truth in the idea that if one will forget his body
in healthy activity, work, and thought, he is not so likely to
become ill. "Your life is what your thoughts make it," said
Marcus Aurelius. But Christian Science has no monopoly of
this religion of healthy-mindedness: Isaiah long ago said that
God would keep in perfect peace the one whose mind was
stayed on Him.[4] Jesus said, "Be not anxious for your life, nor
for your body, nor for the morrow—the Heavenly Father
knows your needs. But seek ye first His kingdom and His
righteousness, and all these things shall be added unto you." [5]
I think there is truer health in this trust in God the Father, no
matter what may come, than there is in denial of sin, sickness,
and death. Christian Science is unreal in its denial of sickness
and suffering.

Snowden is probably correct in saying that this denial of
sickness and suffering came from Mrs. Eddy's unwillingness
to endure: she had to be protected from every annoyance when
she was the leader of a growing sect, even as she did when
she was a girl at home. Her father comforted her in his arms
even after she was grown; she was rocked in a special cradle;
she took this cradle along with her at her marriage and her
husband rocked her in it as though she were a baby. People
who took her into their homes had to pamper her. She had
to be spared any discomfort. This is truly a contrast to the
New Testament ideal of accepting hardships, taking up a cross.
This is too much of a hedonistic philosophy, living for pleasure
and comfort; it is too selfish. Life cannot all be sweet melody

[4] Isaiah 26:3.
[5] Matthew 6:25–33.

and harmony. "God is not simply nursing us in comfort in this world. He is not merely rocking babies, but making men. The world is made of sterner stuff and life is confronted with greater and graver issues than health and comfort. Health is not holiness. Plato and Socrates, Isaiah and Paul, Luther and Lincoln never thought of comfort; and the Son of God was made perfect through suffering and came to the very culmination and climax of His glory on the cross." [6]

Christian Scientists play up their cures: testimonials are part of their meetings and are reported in all their literature. Many people are attracted by this. Yet the Scientists are quite illogical: they deny any reality to disease and death, and affirm that only the good, mind, and God exist. If the disease is not real, logically there can be no cure: it would only be realizing one had made an error in thinking he was sick. Yet, in spite of Mrs. Eddy's denial that the material senses can bear any reliable testimony, she devotes many pages in her *Science and Health* to testimonies of cures from diseases accepted as realities. In spite of such illogical reasoning, there are healings, and people are won to Christian Science. I will later discuss the question of their cures.

Healings do not prove theories. Other healers, who hold to diverse and even conflicting theories of disease and its cure, also report healings. While in Korea I saw many folk who had scars of burns on their abdomens: they had been treated by burning a little pile of "moxa" (powdered dry herbs) over the supposed site of the disease's process. Many of them got well; but this does not prove that they had a "cold" disease to be cured by the heat of burning "moxa." Other sick folk had acupuncture needles thrust into various parts of the body, and

---

[6] James H. Snowden, *The Truth About Christian Science*, p. 266 (Westminster Press, Philadelphia, 1920).

they got well: but this does not prove that the trouble had been a "wind" disease to be cured by acupuncture to let the wind out. Recovery after treatment cannot be taken as proof of the theory of disease and treatment the healer may happen to hold. There is a healing force in nature that tends to health, "vis medicatrix naturae," and people get well regardless of the method of treatment in most cases. Cures are not proof of the theory held by the therapist; they call for study to find the explanation. It took three hundred years of study to find out why "Peruvian bark" (quinine) would cure malaria; cures by its use did not prove that malaria was caused by "bad air," though doctors so believed until the malaria parasites were found in the blood and in mosquitoes. Faith cures, of whatever kind, also must be studied to learn how the cure comes about.

Cures by faith, by prayers, by anointings, by laying on of hands, by suggestion, by hypnotism, by Christian Science, all have a psychic element, just as truly as that of the psycho-therapist. The divergent theories of these various healings, as held by their practitioners, cannot all be true. We believe it is psychic power that is the common factor in these various heal-ing methods, and that this accounts for the cures. Of course I do not mean to deny that God has a part in it: mental healing is in accord with His laws, and is His way of working; in using medicines, I am using what God has given to us, and as a physi-cian I am working with Him; the healing power of nature, "vis medicatrix naturae," is His power. And I believe He works in ways we do not yet comprehend—more of this later.

I cannot discuss Christian Science without some considera-tion of its basic tenets; the very "handiness" of the statements of Mrs. Eddy's beliefs has been a factor in the spread of the cult, says Zweig. For references, I use my copy of Mrs. Eddy's *Science and Health,* 1934 edition.

She says that all real being is in God, the divine Mind; and that since Life, Truth, and Love are all-powerful, the opposites of these can only be the false testimony of our material senses. Hence sin, sickness, disease, death, are errors of mind in matter. This logically means that there is no reality except God. On other pages she speaks of propositions being self-evident because reversible: such as that God is all and nothing is matter, which can be read in reverse, matter is nothing and all is God. Such use of words bespeaks cleverness, but is no proof of truth.

The real appeal in such propositions as the above, is in their emphasis on the "allness of God"—and this idea is iterated and reiterated all through the book as part of what she claimed was a final revelation received by her in 1866. It would be wonderful, if true, that the "allness of God" really made all else unreal, so that pain and suffering, sin and evil, were only errors of mortal mind. But we cannot deny the facts of human experience: sickness and death are real; the Bible recognized them as such; the Master and His apostles considered sufferings to be more than "errors of mortal mind." One cannot really make sense of the Old and New Testaments by denying the reality of evil and sin and death. There is no more difficult problem in theology and philosophy than that of explaining how there can be evil in a universe made by a good God: but it is no solution to deny all reality to evil, sickness, and death, as Christian Science does. We may see a hint of a solution of the problem in the fact that God is making men of character; and without the possibility of choice, even of wrong choices, real men cannot be made. If this be limiting God to thus allow for a degree of human freedom and free will, we believe it is a limit imposed on Him by His own love.

It simply is not true that the cause of all disease is mental, a mortal fear, a mistaken belief, as Mrs. Eddy asserts: no one would claim that germs or bacteria cause all disease; but they do have a lot to do with sickness. The malaria plasmodium and the spirochete of syphilis are more than errors of mortal mind. Even though Mrs. Eddy teaches that if a person changes his mental state, chills and fever will disappear, the mere change of mind is hardly sufficient to kill malaria plasmodia and bring relief to the victim. The cure of syphilis takes more than Christian Science can give. When Mrs. Eddy says that she never knew a patient who did not recover when the belief of the disease had gone, it is quite evident that she did not follow through on case history.

I cannot understand the mental quirk by which she could claim that Christian Science was always the most skilful surgeon and that she knew of cures, by mental surgery alone, of broken bones, dislocated joints, and spinal vertebrae, and yet advise her followers to leave the adjustment of broken bones and dislocations to the fingers of a surgeon. Either the advice or the claim must have been an error of her mortal mind.

I would pass by such foolishness as her comparison of giving a baby a bath to taking a fish out of water and covering it with dirt; but it is like so much else. It is not easy to be respectful in regard to such statements as that the hosts of Aesculapius are flooding the world with diseases because they are ignorant that the human mind and body are myths; or when she says that any poisonous effects of drugs are due to human beliefs. The patient and the physician may expect favorable results, but the beliefs of a vast majority of mankind, even though they know nothing of this particular case, determine the effects of a dose of poison swallowed by mistake, not the infinitesimal minority of opinions in the sick room. It requires a clever mind thus to explain away poisons and all drug actions, but not a logical one.

We readily grant that there have been cures under Christian Science treatment. The emphasis on God and His power and goodness, on health as the normal thing, relieves fears and anxieties; it takes the mind of the sick person from self and his ills; it thus gives the healing powers of nature a chance to work for health. There is a powerful suggestion: negative as to the unreality of disease, and positive as to the power of mind, or Mind, God. The explanations of and exhortations to faith in God, and the attitude and words of the practitioner—or the book—impress the patient to believe in cure, in health. Readings from *Science and Health* reiterate a few basic ideas over and over. Even silent treatment, or "absent treatment," are impressive suggestions: and suggestions have power to arouse the mind. There is virtue in the insistence of Christian Science on the duty of cheerfulness, not giving way to thoughts of ill health; as there is in the saying, "Smile and you will feel like smiling." This helps; but Christian Science has no monopoly on this virtue.

No one knows the proportion of cures and failures under Christian Science treatment. Dr. Richard C. Cabot, of Boston, one of the great medical scientists of the early 1900's, made a study of one hundred reported cures of folk living in or near Boston.[7] He had personal interviews where that was possible, and letters from the persons cured where he could not arrange to see them. Comparing these reports with those of his own patients, he concluded that most cures of Christian Science were probably genuine: but that they were not cures of organic diseases. He found no evidence of cures of cancer or tuberculosis. Most of the cases were self-diagnosed, or were second- or third-hand reports of what some doctor was supposed to

[7] Richard C. Cabot, "One Hundred Christian Science Cures," *McClure's Magazine*, Vol. 31, pp. 472–476 (Aug., 1908).

have said; but no proper diagnostic studies had been made. He further says that he thinks these people made honest mistakes, from "intellectual mistiness"; he does not think they were lying.

In comparing the statements of these "cured" people with his own patient's reports of their illnesses, he reminds us that when a patient tells a doctor he has kidney trouble, it generally turns out that both kidneys are sound; a patient's "heart trouble" usually means some pain on the left side of the chest and no organic disease of the heart at all. His experience had made him realize that a patient who had been to many doctors and been given various diagnoses, was probably suffering from a functional or nervous disease. He says that patients with organic disease seldom go to Christian Science healers; so there is a kind of "natural selection" of functional cases for the practitioners. "Common sense keeps the majority of sufferers from organic diseases away from the parlors of the Christian Scientist."

When I, as a doctor, read Mrs. Eddy's hundred pages of testimonials in *Science and Health*, I was sure any doctor would know many of the cases to have definitely been neuroses, in spite of the diagnoses she reported. In many cases the diagnosis was certainly not what was given; in some cases one did not have enough facts to venture a diagnosis; and in some a doctor simply would not accept as fact the things reported—though granting that the person thought he was telling the truth. Many of the treatments would be known to give only temporary relief, not cures. And often a doctor would have a very good idea as to the nature of the cure of the neurosis. The cures, where genuine, were psychotherapy cures, for Christian Science is one method of psychotherapy, and rather effective for some cases, especially the hysterias. I would not deny that some organic ills were cured: but as I have already said, they were due to the power of mind over body, even to the extent of organic changes toward health.

One must say that deaths do follow Christian Science treatments in some cases: it has been rather notorious that some parents have allowed children to die of diphtheria while trusting in Christian Science. Some of these cases have resulted in police intervention and serious consideration of the need for legislation to prevent such neglect of children. Christian Scientists do die of the same common diseases that afflict the rest of mankind—and Mrs. Eddy herself was not exempt.

Rev. Dr. Charles R. Brown studied in the classes of Mrs. Eddy herself and was a licensed Christian Science practitioner, with his diploma signed and sealed at a cost of $300 for two weeks' tuition.[8] He tells of a case he knew: a child who died of diphtheria; she was allowed to play with other children, because there was "nothing the matter with her, it was only a belief of mortal mind." But the two children next door and their nurse got diphtheria from her. They had antitoxin and recovered promptly—but their suffering and the expense of their sickness were thrust upon them by the Christian Scientists in disregard of the law.[9] Later Mrs. Eddy advised her healers to obey the law in regard to contagious diseases, while insisting that Christian Scientists could handle the most malignant contagion with perfect assurance. One might appropriately ask how such healers can know what kind of diseases their patients have: they simply are not competent to make proper diagnoses.

Another heralded cure was that of a case of tuberculosis: [10]

[8] Charles R. Brown, *Faith and Health*, pp. 76–78 (Thomas Y. Crowell Co., New York, 1924).
[9] *Ibid.*, pp. 110 f.
[10] *Ibid.*, pp. 117 f.

Dr. Brown knew the woman well; everything that money and affection could do for her relief was done; but she did not improve, and wanted to try Christian Science; her husband arranged for this too. For a time she felt better—as such patients often do: a complete cure was celebrated by the Christian Science congregation. But in a few months Dr. Brown conducted her funeral: she had died of tuberculosis. He refers to the claim of Mrs. Eddy to have cured cancer: yet her own sister-in-law, for whom Mrs. Eddy professed great affection, lingered on for years, suffering, and she finally died of cancer of the breast.

Granting that Christian Science has helped a goodly number of people to better health, it is not because of the truth of Christian Science, nor of any excellence of its psychotherapy. Many in the regular churches can testify to physical help by spiritual means. Dr. Brown tells of his own health: as a boy he was always below par physically; but he learned to use forces for recovery in what he calls a "Gospel of Good Health," [11] a practice of religious faith and suggestion. He testifies that for twenty-five years he never missed an appointment as a minister because of sickness. In this, he says, he was "greatly helped by methods of which Christian Science is an awkward, confusing caricature." I am convinced that all the values of Christian Science as a healing method can be better realized by wholesome religion and medical science.

Christian Science is not "science" by any accepted standard meaning of the word. Science is reasoned thinking, based on human experience and observation; it all depends on the reliability of our senses to report truthfully to us. Christian Science denies this reliability of our senses in stating that the material senses cannot bear reliable testimony on the subject of health,

[11] *Ibid.*, pp. 123–124.

and that the mortal body is only an erroneous mortal belief of mind in matter. This leaves no basis for any science—not even Mrs. Eddy's "Divine Science."

A great stretch of tolerance is needful, if one is to grant Christian Science any claim to being "Christian." It does not follow the historic ideas of Christianity; it gives its own and quite unorthodox meanings to words that have had a definite significance to Christians for nineteen hundred years; the sense of New Testament words and passages are quite perverted from their historic meanings; her interpretations of scripture are rarely that of historic Christianity. Mrs. Eddy broke with historic Christianity and claimed to have received her teachings as the final revelation from God of the absolute divine Principle of scientific mental healing. Of course there are truths in *Science and Health* which any Christian readily accepts; but the basic ideas of Mrs. Eddy diverge greatly from the teachings accepted by Christians from the very time of the apostles. One cannot help thinking Mrs. Eddy appropriated words from Christianity and from science without really understanding what the words meant.

Her theories are pantheistic even though she tried to deny it. Her main thesis is the "allness of God." In the New Testament the word "Logos" unquestionably refers to the Christ, but Mrs. Eddy disagrees in stating that the true Logos is demonstrably Christian Science. She rightly speaks of the atonement of Christ as reconciling man to God rather than God to man. But as to His sacrifices and sufferings, she makes the claim that suffering is an error of sinful sense which Truth destroys, and that eventually both sin and suffering will fall at the feet of everlasting Love. One cannot by any stretch of imagination find anything like this in the New Testament account of our Master. She identifies the Holy Spirit with divine Science.

The Comforter is equated with divine Science. Receiving
the Holy Spirit meant that those who had witnessed to Christ
and suffered were aroused to an enlarged understanding of
divine Science, according to Mrs. Eddy. These ideas are totally
foreign to historic Christianity. Her emphasis on healing is
unlike that of the New Testament and of the Church: suffering and disease are considered real, not just errors of mortal
mind, in the New Testament writings and in all the course of
Christianity. A reading of *Science and Health* will truly make
it plain that her "divine Science" is neither Science nor Christian.

NEW THOUGHT

Akin to Christian Science in its origin, and partly so in teachings, is "New Thought." Both came out of the work and
teachings of Phineas P. Quimby, the healer of Mrs. Mary
Baker-Patterson-Glover-Eddy. Mrs. Eddy denied any debt to
Quimby; but in her early days she was an ardent disciple and
advocate of Quimby and his teachings; the basic ideas of her
doctrines follow his lines; scholars do not doubt that she took
her teachings from Quimby, and then made changes of her
own—especially in the illogical denial of sickness and matter
as realities. Associated with Quimby, and with Mrs. Eddy for
a time, was Julius Dresser; he continued a more faithful Quimby
disciple; he became the leader of "New Thought."

New Thought emphasizes the affirmation of the good, of
health, of the divine supply; and along with healing its followers stress spiritual fulness of life, and the application of New
Thought to the practical affairs of life. But they do not deny
matter or sickness, while insisting on the healing power that
is available if man will but trust in God. New Thought is not
a church; its followers are urged to be better members of the

church to which they belong. It makes its approach through the immanence of God, the present available power of God. It seeks to induce a cheerful, confident, serene state of mind, and to remove the attitude of invalidism and negative emotions and beliefs, to promote relaxation and give full play to suggestions or auto-suggestions of health. It respects the traditional Christian teachings, and does not pervert Biblical ideas by allegorizing as does Christian Science. It is a more sane and Christian approach to life; but it seems to me too pantheistic, or theosophical. As a healing cult its influence is not great now; though its most notable book, Trine's *In Tune with the Infinite*, still holds a place on library shelves.

UNITY

Unity is a form of New Thought, and has a much wider influence these days. It does not make as much of healing as does Christian Science. It is like New Thought in its emphasis on success and power in business and social life. Its followers have prayers for healings, and claim cures of a great variety of ills—not the least of them being poverty. In its use of words about God, Unity is similar to Christian Science. Its founder, Charles Fillmore, in *Christian Healing*, writes of the one Presence, one Intelligence, one Substance, and the one Life, the Good Omnipotent. He calls God the Principle in whom we live and move and have our being, and in whom we share His omnipotence. God-Mind is another of his expressions. Man is said to be a Perfect Idea in the God-Mind; this Perfect Idea is the only real man, the true self. Man as Perfect Idea in the God-Mind has back of him all the powers of Being, and there is nothing impossible if he will give the divine Principle full sway and make his thoughts strong enough to carry out what God seeks to express in man.

Unity does not deny the reality of matter or sickness; but Fillmore teaches that man thinks his body into disease, and that the majority of bodily ills have their origin in erroneous thoughts and the misuse of life functions. He propounds some very naïve and unscientific ideas, such as that an "I can't" state of mind is the cause of bodily relaxations, of prolapses, kidney complaints, and dropsy; that these ills are to be healed by affirmation of the divine power working in us; and that the habit of being critical and indulging in severe judgments on our fellows produces torpidity of the liver. He taught that every thought produces its microbe: disease, sin, selfishness, anger, hate, avarice, lust, poverty—each after its kind. But Unity has now dropped this from its publications.

While Unity does emphasize healing, my limited reading leads me to believe that they put as much, or more, stress on success. Gatlin, in *God Is the Answer*, another of the Unity texts, challenges their followers to declare they are not going to be sick and will be well, and are well now, healed by the wholeness of God. He also says that if they will assert that they are not and will not be poor, they may rely on God, who is everywhere-present substance to make Himself evident in all their affairs. The greater part of Gatlin's book is given over to the success idea—along with some really good Christian teachings as to the present working of God in human life, and our need to trust God in all things. In spite of the bizarre and unfounded teachings of the founder, Fillmore, Unity does have in general a Christian approach to life and its problems.

There is a secondary emphasis on healing in the groups called "Pentecostal"; but their major teachings are on the baptism and infilling of the Holy Ghost. Some of them practice healing by prayers, by laying on of hands, or by anointing, faith healing; but this is secondary.

One of the more prominent leaders of healing cults was Aimee Semple-McPherson-Rolfe: whatever be one's judgment of her, we have to admit that she made a great success of her healing cult. Some think she was simply a charlatan, consciously dishonest, preying on the gullible; some consider her sincere but self-deluded; some think of her as primarily an actress who put on colorful pageants that attracted thousands; many believe she was truly a great religious leader. In any case, one of her greatest attractive powers was the healing services when she prayed for the sick, the crippled, the maimed, the blind. There can be no question that many people did leave their crutches and walk from the tabernacle; many did profess to be healed of all sorts of illnesses—and the money flowed in. So far as I know, there has never been a consistent follow-up of those who professed to be cured; undoubtedly many relapsed and died of the sickness they thought had been cured; but not all. The "Four-Square Church," founded by Mrs. McPherson, has its members by the thousands throughout the southwest. Since her death from an overdose of sleeping pills, the work is being carried on in the name of her son; but there is not now the publicity given to this cult that there was during the days of Mrs. McPherson's dramatic adventures.

IV

Healings and the Church

PLACE OF HEALING IN HISTORIC CHRISTIANITY

From the beginning Christianity has recognized the reality of sickness, and has in some measure practiced healing. It began with the healing ministry of the Master: this is a fact of history acknowledged by His friends and His enemies, by the Talmud as well as by the New Testament.[1] His healings, the "miracles," are so truly integral parts of His work that they cannot be taken out of the Gospel accounts; they were one of the great attractions for the multitudes that followed Him. Healings by the apostles and their successors in the early church are taken for granted by the earliest Christian writers. The apostles took His command to heal the sick as part of their commission to go into all the world, to preach, to teach, and to heal.

Yet we must recognize that Jesus did not allow healing of the sick to displace the proclamation of the gospel as His major emphasis: for Him the central thing was spiritual, not physical. At times He turned away from the crowds demanding healing, to go off with His disciples to teach them. His time could very easily have been filled with works for the physical welfare of men: but then it would not have been a continuing, growing

[1] I acknowledge my indebtedness to Charles F. Kemp, *Physicians of the Soul*, pp. 24–38 (The Macmillan Co., New York), for data in this chapter.

thing as it has been for two thousand years. He turned from the temptation to make a physical ministry, and a spectacular ministry His life work at the time He was tempted in the wilderness. As time went on, He gave less and less of His time to healing and more to teaching and preaching. He healed the sick of divers diseases, and also those "possessed of evil spirits," because He was moved with compassion, and "Himself took our infirmities and bare our diseases," [2] but this was not His mission; He came to do a deeper and more vital thing—to save the whole man, and all men.

As we look at the accounts of the early church, we see a decreasing emphasis on healings: after the first few chapters of the book of Acts there is little reference to miracles of healing. The exhortation is to seek spiritual gifts rather than healings. In the list of the gifts of the Spirit given by Paul (I Cor. 12:14) healing came in for only incidental mention; he said too many were seeking to speak with tongues and neglecting the more excellent gifts; the rivalry seemed to be between "tongues" and "prophecy"—and by prophecy, Paul meant not foretelling but forthright speaking, as in preaching. As Charles Reynolds Brown points out,[3] the seer of Revelation saw, "The leaves of the tree were for the healing of the nations." The main business of a tree is to produce fruit, leaves are incidental to the main function. The apostles did heal the sick; but they gave themselves to the main spiritual ministry, to the fundamental thing. The healing ministry was recognized as a part of the work of the church, at least until the time of Augustine— many never gave it up.

The care of the sick has always been recognized as a vital

[2] Matthew 8:17.
[3] Charles R. Brown, *Faith and Health*, p. 215 (Thomas Y. Crowell Co., New York, 1910).

function of the church: but it appears to have taken the form of providing shelter and nursing, along with care of the hungry, the homeless, the unemployed, the naked, and all those in need. Christians founded hospitals and homes, even for lepers. When monasteries were established one of the works was that of caring for the sick and the orphaned. Some of the orders had this for their special task; and in time the "Sisters of Charity" were pledged never to refuse care of the sick no matter how loathsome the disease or how dangerous. But all this seems more of nursing and ministering to the sick rather than of healing. The practice of healing by prayer, by laying on of hands, by anointing, was neglected but not lost; after the primitive church, healings were more often attributed to relics of the saints, or to shrines. Just as there are healings at shrines in our day, like Lourdes, throughout the Christian era there have always been healings.

There have also been cures attributed to great religious leaders in days of intense religious enthusiasm. Faith cures are attributed to Luther and other leaders of the Reformation. A contemporary writer tells of Luther's cure of his great fellow-worker, Philip Melanchthon. These leaders had given dubious consent to a marriage considered bigamous; Melanchthon was so filled with remorse over it that he became very ill, and his life was despaired of; Luther was called. "When Luther arrived he found Melanchthon apparently dying; his eyes were sunk, his sense gone, his speech stopped, his hearing closed, his face fallen in and hollow, as Luther said, 'Facies erat Hippocratica.' He knew nobody, he drank nothing. When Luther saw him thus disfigured, he was frightened above measure and said to his companions, 'God forfend, how has the devil defaced this organon.' He then turned to the window and prayed fervently to God. . . . Hereupon he grasped Philip by the hand: 'Be

of good courage, Philip, thou shalt not die; give no place
to the spirit of sorrow, and be not thine own murderer, but
trust in the Lord.' Then Philip by degrees became more cheerful and let Luther order him something to eat, and Luther himself brought it to him, and Philip refused it. Then Luther forced
him with these threats, saying, 'Hark, Philip, thou must eat,
or I excommunicate thee.' With these words he was so overcome that he ate a very little and thus by degrees he gained his
strength again." [4]

Cures attended the rise of the Quaker movement and of the
Baptists in the seventeenth century; healings were reported in
the Methodist revival of the eighteenth century. Sporadic
healing movements have been reported with increasing fre-
quency throughout the nineteenth century and up to our time.
Now the Federal Council of Churches reports in its bulletin
that there is a religion and health movement of ecumenical
character going on in the churches.

There has been much discussion as to why the "age of miracles" ended soon after the apostles. Some have claimed that the
need for miracles was past when Christianity became the accepted religion of the Roman empire; that healings were only
a passing phase of the work of the church. Others, probably
more nearly correct, claimed that it was because the church
leaders, busy with routine church affairs and organization,
gradually neglected the healing ministry; as Christians became
worldly they lost the power to heal. There are many who insist that the spiritual power for healing is available now to any
who will pay the price of devotion; that religious healing has
not ceased, that it is being practiced now as it has been by a

[4] Elwood Worcester, Samuel McComb, and J. H. Coriat, *Religion and
Medicine*, pp. 310 f. (Moffat, Yard & Co., New York, 1908. Reprinted by
permission of Dodd, Mead & Co., New York).

few through the ages. These say it is not for us to argue about the history of healings and miracles, but that we should rather seek to learn how we may receive this gift, how God may work in and through us to heal.

WHAT ABOUT MIRACLES?

Stories of miracles and wonders are common in all ancient religions: the minds of primitive peoples are quite animistic, and they see no inconsistency in miracles even though contrary to natural law. They have not attained to any idea of natural law; and natural events seem to them to be interventions of spirits or demons, or the very gods. We also know that stories grow as they get further away from the actual events: and we may accept the view that this is true of some of the Bible miracles; but this does not mean that we must reject the Bible for this reason any more than that we should do so because its science is out of date. Some of the miracle stories we simply cannot accept as literal facts: we may doubt that even Elisha could make an ax come up out of the water and float; but we can see in the story something of the esteem he acquired as years passed. We have gotten away from the idea that miracles are contrary to the laws of nature: we think of them rather as events in which divine power has been used for moral ends in ways we do not yet understand. But we know enough to believe that they are not magical, capricious displays of power; rather they are truly in line with the laws of nature and nature's God. We have to admit that our knowledge lacks much of being complete; the more we learn of natural laws, the more we can do that was impossible to former generations.

Not long ago, scientists "proved" that it would be impossible for heavier-than-air machines to stay in the air, to fly: but the Wright brothers utilized their knowledge of scientific laws, and they did fly. We now take air travel as a matter of course. To sit at home and hear over the radio the words of General MacArthur in Tokyo Bay would have been more of a miracle to people of Jesus' day than to see healing miracles. And as we learn more of science we are not only hearing but seeing events as they occur; and we expect television soon to let us see things in color—as I have actually done at medical conventions. In one of my medical journals, I read of a young man blinded after using a submachine gun on an attacker; after treatment in a hospital he recovered sight, but later he had a second blind spell. This time the eye doctor used psychotherapy, and the young man went away seeing. We do not call this a miracle, for we understand something of the psychogenic origin of his blindness and the rationale of the treatment, but it would have been a miracle to our ancestors. As we gain more knowledge, we get glimpses of laws that make the reported miracles of the Christ credible.

To me it seems impossible to remove the accounts of miracles out of the gospels without destroying them: the miracles and narratives of other events are woven together. I am glad that we are not called on to defend everything in the Bible from Genesis to Revelation: we may admit errors in history, and contradictions, and believe that some of the stories grew with the years; yet the Bible is the source book for our knowledge of Jesus Christ, and He is Christianity, its very soul. He Himself is a greater miracle than the works reported. We do not need the miracles as evidence for Him, to confirm our faith in Him. It is remarkable that formerly Christian apologists appealed to the miracles as proofs of His divinity, and now we believe that His character and personality make the miracles credible. Our glimpses into scientific laws and our expanding knowledge give us ever-increasing power to do things that are more like His marvellous works; yet we recognize that He is unique, far surpassing us, so we grant Him power beyond our own. We believe He was working in full accord with the laws of God and nature in what He did, while on earth, to help and heal men: He said, "My Father worketh hitherto; and I work." [5]

The more I understand of the laws of nature and the laws of human relations, including the body and mind of men, the more I see how truly He knew what is in man. The more I know of modern science, the more I see His wisdom. His teachings and His personality reveal to mankind the very laws of nature and of nature's God. He was not giving arbitrary commandments when He told us to love, to do good, to lose self; He was telling us the only way that nature's God and natural laws will allow men to be truly healthy and happy. He was giving us the laws of good living, just as really as hygiene tells us how to live healthy physical lives. He was so far in advance of even our modern day in His social science and mental hygiene that I believe He had powers the rest of us do not have. He Himself, in His life, His resurrection, His ever-present power, is the greatest miracle. He himself makes His works seem credible. My faith in Him makes me believe that we have not yet half realized the help He can give us in our spiritual and physical lives. God was in Christ, and He is still working in the hearts of men, able to do more than we ask or think.

CHURCH HOSPITALS

I have already written of the care of the sick by Christians from the very early days of the church. Wealthy converts established hostels where the sick could be cared for; bishops and leaders of the church raised money to build and support

[5] John 5:17.

hospitals. Almost the only hospitals were those of the Christian church. There were few places that could by any stretch of the word be called "hospitals" before Christianity, and those were in connection with shrines and temples, such as the temples of Aesculapius, with physician-priests in attendance. King Asoka of India is reported to have established hospitals for his people. But I think it is only fair to credit the Christian church with the spread of hospitals all over the world: in modern times there were no hospitals outside Christendom until recently when governments have copied church hospitals. A few Buddhist hospitals and homes have also been established—certainly due to Christian example. In the West, until governments began to build hospitals, there were none except those of the church; and it was not until the eighteenth century that city governments started this movement. It is only recently that secular hospitals have been at all common: and we may at least claim that part of the credit for this is due to the permeation of society by the Christian spirit.

There is a new ministry in the church hospitals that is rapidly spreading: that of direct spiritual ministry to the sick, along with the best of medical, surgical, and nursing care. There is more of prayer and spiritual counselling for the sick, and many hospitals are now having ministers on the staff, to direct this use of religion for the healing of sick bodies and souls in the hospital beds. As ministers, priests, sisters, and nurses learn more of the modern use of psychology and psychotherapy in their conselling of patients, we may expect the spiritual results to improve along with better healing. But we do not expect them to become psychiatrists or psychologists: they are bringers of religion to the sick, parts of a team that endeavors to help the whole of the sick person, soul as well as body. Our hospitals are offering religious psychotherapy, with emphasis on the religion.

MEDICAL MISSIONS

Another phase of the healing ministry of the church is the work of medical missions of the past hundred and more years. The first concern of the church in its missionary work was to save souls, to Christianize the world. But when the early missionaries came face to face with the sufferings of the people of mission lands, even without medical training they began to render a crude medical service to the sick—it was better than anything otherwise available in those lands. Before long the mission boards sent out physicians and surgeons, and provided hospitals and clinics; ultimately they established medical schools and nurses' training schools. Medical missions led in teaching hygiene and sanitation, preventive health work. Health leaflets, booklets, and books have been written, printed, and passed out to patients; classes in personal and public health have been taught. Mothers have been taught how to care for their children, and this has helped to reduce the appalling infant mortality and suffering of these lands. They introduced vaccination into lands where it was said that parents did not count their children till after they had had the smallpox. Plagues and epidemics have been overcome—now largely by government agencies that have taken up the work begun by medical missionaries.

Medical missions has been a great opener of doors: Peter Parker said he was opening China "with the point of a lancet." A doctor opened the door for missionary work in Korea, where I served for more than twenty years. It has opened doors to many hearts as well, as people saw Christian love in action, and skill such as they had never dreamed of, freely serving the least and the lowliest. But it was not just a means to gain hearers of the gospel and converts: it was itself an expression of the spirit of the Christ who was moved with compassion for distressed people.

CHURCHES WITH HEALING EMPHASIS

The never lost, but much-neglected idea of religious healing is coming to the fore again—as I have said. I believe this is in part due to the rise and success of Christian Science; the church has been stimulated to recover a realization of the New Testament emphasis on body *and* soul. Christian Science is the only large body placing its primary emphasis on healing; but many groups have arisen that hold divine healing as one of their tenets. In general they are of the Pentecostal type and make much of the emotional side of religion. A long list of these groups is given in the religious census tables of the U.S. Census Bureau: prominent among them are various groups called "Church of God" or "Assemblies of God." The Nazarene Church is probably the largest of these groups. So far as I know, these churches put healings secondary to their emphasis on the work of the Holy Ghost, and on holiness. They recognize the reality of sickness, and sin is very real to them. They are truly in the line of historic Christianity—though one may regret their undue emotionalism, or their stress on certain doctrines.

Attention has been called to the fact that these groups are almost all of recent origin, after the rise of Christian Science; thus Christian Science was for a time without significant competition in this field. But it is also worthy of note that they have arisen and spread among an entirely different class of people, as to economic, cultural, and social background. Christian Science is almost entirely urban and composed of the more favored classes; these other groups are more from the under-privileged and dispossessed people, folk to whom emotional religion makes an especial appeal. The ecstatic expressions of religion give these people a feeling of nearness to God, and a keen expectancy of His help; many of them have never had adequate medical care, and some have had none; when sick, they got well or died, dependent on nature's powers. It is to be expected that they would make much of prayer and faith healing—partly as compensation for their ills; and it is among the less sophisticated folk of all lands that faith healing in various forms prevails. Christian Science, on the contrary, is a group composed of people more subject to nervous and neurotic disorders, and consequently more amenable to psychotherapy.

EMMANUEL MOVEMENT

Another noteworthy movement for religious healing arose in the Episcopal Church and in Boston. Is there any significance in the fact that it started near the Mother Church of Christian Science? The leaders of the Emmanuel movement were ministers of the Emmanuel Episcopal Church in Boston. Dr. Elwood Worcester had been a professor of psychology, after study with Wundt in Germany; Dr. Samuel McComb had studied psychology in Oxford. Dr. Worcester credits the inspiration for this venture into religious therapy to his friend, Dr. S. Weir Mitchell, the famous psychiatrist. He consulted with other medical scientists in Boston, among them Dr. Cabot of Harvard and Dr. Coriot of Tufts Medical College, and with Dr. Barker of Johns Hopkins; these doctors all approved the plan and gave coöperation. It was Worcester's plan to deal only with patients whose disorder was functional, and after medical men had given express approval in each case. He believed that religion had something to contribute in helping the sick, by dealing with spiritual problems as well as physical ills; he thought Christianity had lost something in its failure to deal with sickness directly, as it had done when it was new.

The ministers, Drs. Worcester and McComb, spent much time in personal consultations with the sick who came to them for help on their doctor's advice; this was individual counselling. They also held weekly meetings for their patients which were classes on health: they had physicians lead discussions on such topics as Worry, Anger, Habit, Insomnia, Nervousness, Suggestion, What the Will Can Do, What Prayer Can Do. There was also opportunity for testimonies, for questions, and for fellowship, as well as for prayer and Scripture reading. The title of a book they published gives a good idea of what they were trying to do: *Religion and Medicine*. They were attempting to add the resources of religion to that of medicine for the healing of the whole man.

The first class they conducted in Emmanuel Church was one for victims of tuberculosis, poor folk who could not hope to go to the Adirondacks or to Arizona for treatment in a sanatorium. They were given instruction on how to care for themselves, and how to avoid spreading the infection to others; they were taught to sleep outdoors on a porch or fire-escape and, if that were not possible, to make an appliance to fit in their windows so they could breathe outdoor air though the body was indoors. They were given encouragement and hope, and religious help, to meet the very hard struggle for health and life. Other classes for the nervous and mentally distressed were given—something like what is now called "group therapy." Along with the personal religious counselling, these folk received medical advice from their own doctors. There was no attempt to limit or oppose the use of drugs and physical treatments; they believed God could use medicines and surgery and physiotherapy just as truly as He could use suggestion and prayer. The God who gives sunshine, fresh air, nourishing food, and pure water for health and healing, can also use quinine or other medicines for healing. They believed in the power of mind over body, and also in medicine, good habits, and in a wholesome, well-regulated life. They did not think it more pious to undertake healing by prayer than to make use of what God has given us through medical science.

The heart of their work was in the individual counselling done by the leaders. Dr. Worcester said that a "constant procession of men and women passed through my study. I ate when I could. I tried to give myself to each of these persons as if I had nothing else to live for, to enter into their problems and sufferings with understanding and sympathy, not to hurry them and not allow them to waste my time." [6] Most of their treatments were counsellings and suggestions, but on occasion they would use hypnosis or deep relaxation—it was psychotherapy with a religious emphasis. This work was continued at Emmanuel Church for twenty-five years; finally Dr. Worcester resigned the rectorship to give his time to private counselling. Let me cite some of the many cases they report helped:

A woman had been suffering from severe headaches for fifty-five years; they had been so agonizing that she was not able to care for her sick daughter, and even for the daughter's funeral she was unable to leave home. This pain had afflicted her four or five days a week for all these years; Dr. Worcester believed the original cause of the pain was gone and that it was only psychic. She was suffering acutely when she came to him; he comfortably seated her and got her quiet; then laying

[6] Elwood Worcester, *Life's Adventure*, p. 290 (Charles Scribner's Sons, New York, 1932).

his hands on her head, he assured her the pain was diminishing, that it was disappearing, and that in ten minutes it would be gone never to return. The suggestion succeeded and the pain punctually ceased and did not return. He does not tell what religious ministry he gave her to get her quiet for the laying on of hands, but the very laying of his hands on her head was a suggestion of religious significance.[7]

He tells of a cultured woman, a guest at the inauguration of a college president: she asked Dr. Worcester to walk with her about the campus, but she soon had to stop and sit down, completely fatigued; she gave a long recital of disabilities and sorrows. She then asked for a statement of the beliefs and methods of Dr. Worcester; but she countered with the statement that she and her husband were "scientific agnostics" and were not interested in religious faith. He replied by asking her what good she thought she was in the world, not able to work, not able to walk, not even able to sleep at night, never a mother and never could be, and unable to be what she wished to be for her husband. He told her that her scientific agnosticism could not help in any of these things. He challenged her to put his religious beliefs to a scientific test of a month, and see if it would not make a profound change in her life. The test was that she should every day retire alone for five minutes and ask, with what faith she could command, that God would reveal His existence in her heart with power. She did not promise, but left him. Five years later, he met her again, a fine-looking woman, with bright eyes and face, carrying herself gracefully. When he did not recognize her, she was gratified; for she was truly a changed woman, younger-looking, vigorous, radiant, instead of the pale, feeble, heavy-eyed, badly poised woman of five years before. She told him how she had tried to carry out the

[7] Retold from Worcester, McComb, and Coriat, *op. cit.*, p. 55.

test, in spite of the discouragement her husband gave her. Then near the end of the month, on a dark, stormy day, weak and deeply depressed, alone, suddenly her heart was filled with a loving light, and she knew she was a changed woman. She helped her husband to the same faith and assurance of the spiritual life. She waited five years to be sure before telling Dr. Worcester.[8]

Dr. Richard C. Cabot made a study of the cures of the Emmanuel Movement and found an encouraging percentage of lasting cures, in a variety of illnesses; there were some failures too. There can be no question that these men did much good to many people. They were exceptionally qualified for such psycho-religious work; they worked in close coöperation with doctors. This movement shows positively that there is value in religious ministry to the sick. But we cannot believe that many ministers would be qualified as they were for this kind of work: possibly they went too far into psychotherapy, out of the proper sphere of the clergy. But I want to point out that it was as religious counsellors that they did most of their work and, though it may not have been as spectacular as some of the other movements, it shows the power of religion for healing.

MINISTERS AND PSYCHO-RELIGIOUS HEALING

There are a great number of ministers doing this kind of work now; some of them are outstanding, well-known men. Their emphasis is on counselling rather than on healing sickness; but they do help many sick folk whose ills are psychogenic—particularly when guilt, fears, anxieties, spiritual problems are large factors. Conspicuous among ministers doing this type of work we may mention Weatherhead of London, Bon-

[8] Retold from Elwood Worcester, *Making Life Better*, pp. 166 f. (Charles Scribner's Sons, New York, 1933).

nell and Peale of New York, and E. Stanley Jones of every-where. Russell L. Dicks is a leader of this religious ministry to the sick and in training theological students for it.

Bonnell quotes a surgeon in New York as saying to him, "Tens of thousands of people visit the clinics and hospitals and offices of physicians in this city every day, seeking a remedy for physical ills. There are as many sick souls in the city who do not come to us medical men, for we don't give them what they need. You clergymen should be constantly at work min-istering to them, even to those whose bodies we treat mechani-cally." [9] There certainly is a broad hint that many people should go to their pastor or some other wise minister just as they would go to a doctor.

Weatherhead tells how he came to get into this line of work.[10] Two ministers were visiting in a hospital ward in Mesopo-tamia during the first World War. A fine Christian doctor who practiced psychotherapy came to them and said, "You padres ought to be doing most of this." Weatherhead then set himself to five years of study of psychology; he found that without trespassing on the spheres of either physicians or psychiatrists there was a place in which he could render a real service as a man of religion. He calls this part of his work "psycho-religious therapy." It is an invitation to common folk to seek the help that religion has to offer them for health and for healing. Such men as he can render a real spiritual service to anxious, wor-ried, troubled, bitter, resentful, guilty sick folk, as well as to the healthy.

Somewhere I read a story that brings out another phase of the need for psycho-religious therapy. A surgeon had suc-

[9] John S. Bonnell, *Pastoral Psychiatry*, p. 51 (Harper & Brothers, New York, 1938).

[10] Leslie Weatherhead, *Psychology in Service of the Soul*, p. xvi (The Macmillan Co., New York, 1930).

cessfully operated on a woman, but she did not rally from the operation; instead she grew worse, until her life was despaired of. There was one unfavorable symptom from the beginning: she evinced no desire to live. At length she turned to the surgeon and said, "Doctor, are you prepared to be physician to the soul as well as to the body?" He was a genuine Christian man and able to be physician to the soul. After the patient had unburdened her mind by confession, she began to mend, and soon was a well woman. Fortunate the sick person who has a doctor who can render this service too; but it need not be a medical man; it may be a minister, a friend, or anyone who is trusted. I have been more than glad when I have been asked to be with people before and during and after their ordeal of operations; and I know others feel the same way about it. We should not hesitate to ask for religious help at such times, and we ought to be more alert to the need in our friends.

The chief anesthetist of a large hospital, a doctor of twenty-five years' experience in this work, says: "For a long time I have observed the mental and spiritual attitudes of patients coming to the operating room. . . . I have noticed that persons with a strong religious faith have far less dread of the operation beforehand, and a smaller measure of surgical shock after the operation. Patients who go to the operating-table with a confident faith in God take less anesthetic, recover from it more easily and with far less of the usual distressing after-effects." [11] This is great testimony to the power of religious faith for the sick. What could be more strengthening in the weakness of sickness than such confident faith utterances as "The Lord is my shepherd; I shall not want. . . . He leadeth me . . . through the valley of the shadow of death. . . . I will fear no evil for Thou art with me"!

[11] Bonnell, *op. cit.*, p. 203.

DOCTORS SEND PATIENTS TO CHURCH

Another indication of the place of the church in the healing ministry is the fact that some doctors are frankly telling their patients they need what the church has to give them—even prescribing church attendance. True the number of such doctors is small; but I have no doubt that many of my medical colleagues realize their own helplessness with many of their patients, and really do believe religion would help more than medicines in many cases. Norman Vincent Peale tells of a very successful physician who often gives such a prescription. One woman he had known for a long time came to him for treatment; she was the kind of patient who goes from doctor to doctor and never does what the doctors tell her. At first he refused to take her case; when she insisted, he made her sign a paper agreeing to do exactly as he told her without argument. Then he gave her some pink pills, then some white pills; then he gave her a prescription carefully written out as if for medicines: "Go to church at least once a Sunday for the next three months." She protested that that was the silliest thing she ever heard of, and that she would not do it. When faced by her signed agreement, and told she must either do it or he would quit her case, she grudgingly agreed to follow directions; it was some time before she began to yield herself to the mood of a service of worship and its healing atmosphere. But finally she found herself interested; she became docile; her resentments went out, and health came in.[12]

This doctor had found that in church worship where they provide for a period of quietness, patients received a new spirit of peace. This is not just a time for vacant minds; the mind and

[12] Norman Vincent Peale, *A Guide to Confident Living*, pp. 1-3 (Prentice-Hall, New York, copyright, 1948).

soul are to be opened to the creative power of God, to His recreative spirit. If one finds himself where there is no provision for this silence before God, he can make it in his own heart, even while other things are being done in church; but the prayer time is truly a time for this. It is a rather frequent suggestion I give to my patients who seem to me to need spiritual help more than medical. Many churches now provide for a quiet time in their program: I regret that all do not, and that in many it is altogether too brief.

TRAINING MINISTERS FOR PSYCHO-RELIGIOUS WORK

The training of theological students and young ministers for psycho-religious work is a sign of that new religion and health movement of ecumenical character going on in the churches, to which we have referred. The study courses in theological schools have been revised enough to allow students to learn psychology as a science and as a practical thing; they are taught how to be counsellors to distracted and troubled and suffering people. This is a renewed emphasis on the person-to-person work of the minister, that he may be qualified to help people before they get sick, and be a wise comforter of the sick—in the true meaning of the words, "one who gives strength." All theological students are now given something in this line, and they will be able to be counsellors for good health and healing.

But it is not alone in this work in the schools, in which Russell L. Dicks is the outstanding leader; there is a further line of work, first started by Anton T. Boisen. He became the chaplain in a State Mental Hospital after special preparation and experience in working with the sick and with the mentally unbalanced; he arranged for four young students to join him to learn at firsthand how to deal with people. The work grew;

and a sort of interneship for theological students was provided, something like that for medical students. A Council for Clinical Training of Theological Students was organized, with doctors and theologians as members. They have been giving a limited number of young ministers work in mental and general hospitals and clinics, and in prisons and corrective institutions. It seems to me that this offers a great hope for the future of the religion and health movement; it is an index of how the church is preparing to render an even more effective ministry to sick and troubled persons, both in soul and in body.

V

The Curative Power of Religion

RELIGION AND THE UNCONSCIOUS

I believe there is a curative power in religion beyond that of simple faith; faith may be set on many things besides God— as we showed in a previous chapter. Faith, as such, does have a therapeutic value; and suggestion in its many forms is curative when directed aright. But there is a value in religion beyond this, in its power for health and healing. The scientific basis for this belief is the theme of this chapter.

As we have already said, the psychogenic factors of illness are not commonly consciously known and recognized. Though some may be fully known to the patient, those that cause most harm are below the level of consciousness. It is at the level of the subconscious, or the unconscious, that religion works most effectively. Gerhard Adler, a pupil of Jung, well says: "Religion is rooted in the unconscious, elemental level in us, and it is from this primordial part of our psyche that the religious images and symbols spring forth. . . . Religion is not a substitute for something else, but it stands right at the beginning of man's existence as man, it is the primal urge of his specific human situation." He emphasizes the psychic reality of religious experience, without discussing the question of the reality of God; he insists that it is an experience common to all the human race, and in all times; it comes out of the "collective unconscious," one of the "archtypes" pre-existent in us.[1] I recall hearing Dr. Alex Hrdlička, head of the anthropological section of the Smithsonian Institution, editor of *Anthropology*, tell that the earliest human relics give evidence of religious beliefs. And it is in these very depths of human nature that religion does its work; at the very level where our psychogenic ills arise. I think Stanley Jones is right when he says that it is in the subconscious that the Holy Spirit does His work.[2]

AFTER INSIGHT, RELIGION IS NEEDED

Insight seems to be the great thing in psychotherapy: one is amazed at the way many people recover from their illnesses when they gain insight as to its cause and origin. It sometimes seems that all there is to psychotherapy is to get the patient to recognize what is underlying his symptoms; this is the basic thing in psychoanalysis, and when the complex is exposed the patient gets well—but not always, for he may not make the adjustments the insight demands. But one is greatly impressed by the many times recovery follows promptly after insight.

When insight is followed by the proper reintegration and the needed action, healing may be surprisingly quick. One of my cases will show this. A man had been having stomach trouble for a good many years, with occasional severe cramps and pains. One day after a hard time in the office, he did not take time for a proper evening meal, and had another severe attack. After a few days of treatment to give relief, and after getting the colon well cleaned out, he was about again. We then made X-ray studies of the entire gastro-intestinal tract, and no serious condition was found; there was no sign of ulcer or

[1] Gerhard Adler, *Studies in Analytical Psychology*, pp. 186–187 (W. W. Norton & Co., New York, 1948).

[2] E. Stanley Jones, *Abundant Living*, p. 152 (copyright, 1942, by Whitmore & Stone—permission of Abingdon-Cokesbury Press, Nashville).

cancer, only a doubtful colitis. He was shown the X-ray films and the pathologist's report. He then confessed that he had been fearing cancer, or at least an ulcer. He was given advice as to diet, eating habits, and general hygiene; he has had no recurrence of the old trouble now in more than five years. The insight he gained saved him from invalidism.

The value of insight and adjustment is well shown in a story I heard Dr. Alvarez tell to a group of doctors. A woman had been a schoolteacher for a good many years, and being tired of that life, had accepted an offer of marriage from a widower; but her high ideals of married love were crushed by the attitude and actions of her rather crude husband. She was disgusted with her experiences; and before long was suffering from various ills. She endured this for two years; the bitterness and sickness finally drove her to the doctor. The whole story of her symptoms and pains and grief and disappointment was poured out. She was rather taken aback when the doctor asked her if she would like to get away from it all by going back to her old life as teacher. She quickly decided that she preferred a husband, even the disappointing one she had, to the life of an old maid schoolteacher. She carried on in her married life and lost her symptoms, her sickness. She had achieved insight as to her troubles and made a reintegration.

The aim of psychotherapy is to help the patient gain sufficient insight into his troubles to make a satisfactory adjustment to them and to life, to face up to their conflicts. This makes a demand on the sick person: he must do what is needed for his cure; he must face up to life with different attitudes and emotions; he cannot leave it all up to the doctor and expect the doctor to make him well. He may be in a situation that cannot be greatly changed, he must live on in the same old environment; but he can do it with new emotions and purposes, and keep well. It is here that religion can render great help.

Some fail to recover simply because of unwillingness or inability to make the necessary adjustments in his own self and in his life situation, to face life properly. This was first brought to my attention as a formulated statement in one of Jung's books. He tells of a highly intelligent young man who came to him with a detailed self-analysis worked out in a form that would have been fit for publication. This young man had studied medical and psychological literature and had an intelligent understanding of his neurosis. According to his— and a very common—understanding, all he needed for a cure was insight; so he asked Jung why he was not cured. If one could grant that insight is all one needs, this young man should have been well; but since he was not cured, Jung supposed his attitude to life must be fundamentally wrong. Inquiry into his history brought out the fact that he spent his winters at St. Moritz or Nice. Asked how he could afford this luxury, and who paid for his holidays, the young man confessed that he got the money from a poor schoolteacher who deprived herself to indulge him; she loved him and sacrificed her own comforts to give him luxuries. Jung well says, "His want of conscience was the cause of his neurosis. . . . His fundamental error lay in his moral attitude." He was shocked at Jung's "unscientific way of looking at things"; he would not even admit to any conflicts about it; for he said she gave him the money of her own free will. He needed some of the good moral sense that religion will give, what Jung called a "religious outlook"; and without it he was not cured.[3] We may here recall our first reference to Jung: he said all his patients in the second half of life

[3] C. G. Jung, *Modern Man in Search of a Soul*, pp. 223–224 (Harcourt, Brace & Co., New York, 1933).

had the problem of finding a religious outlook on life; they fell ill because they had lost what religion has to give, and none had been cured who did not regain a religious outlook.

Jung also says in another place that the doctor may clearly see why his patient is ill: "It arises from his having no love, but only sexuality; no faith, because he is afraid to grope in the dark; no hope, because he is disillusioned by the world and by life; and no understanding, because he has failed to read the meaning of his own existence." [4] It is in religion that one may find true love, true faith and hope, true understanding. Psychotherapy, as such, needs religion to supplement it.

Bonnell tells of a man who came to him after having completed twelve psychotherapeutic treatments; but he had to find religious help before he was free of his troubles. At the end of his last interview with the psychiatrist, he was told, "Now you understand your problem, don't you?" When he said he understood, the psychiatrist said, "Well, now proceed under your own steam." But the patient confessed that his trouble was "not having any steam left." He realized the relation of his trouble to the unwise care of a nursemaid when he was a small child, that his behavior was an "infantile regression," and was wrecking his life. When he was urged to receive a new power, "the expulsive power of a new affection," he asked, "How can I receive this power?" Dr. Bonnell helped him truly to turn to the Lord in faith; he did so and became a free man, "no longer interested in this sordid business." He was followed up for three years with no recurrences. It was religion that was added to insight to give this man health.[5]

For these ills medicine and surgery have little value; going to

---

[4] *Ibid.*, p. 260.

[5] John S. Bonnell, *Psychology for Pastor and People*, pp. 29 f. (Harper & Brothers, New York, 1948).

the seashore or to the mountains for rest will not avail when the sick person carries his burdens, conflicts, anxieties, fears, hates, and guilt along in his soul. It is not expected that a physician or surgeon or psychiatrist will deal with his patients on definitely religious lines. This needs a "physician of the soul." Medical men are not trained for such work; if they do assure anxious, fearful souls, suffering from guilt, of the love and goodness and power of God, it will not be as medical men but because they have religion in their own hearts and speak as man to man. This is truly a work for the clergy and religious workers; they should prepare for it; and people should go to them for help as "physicians of the soul." Psychiatrists are encroaching on the sphere of religious counsellors if they preëmpt this part of the ministry to the sick. This is the place for what Weatherhead calls "psycho-religious healing"; it is religious therapy in accord with scientific psychological technique. The religious worker properly leaves physical symptoms to the medical profession; but he does have concern with the spiritual disharmony of the sick person. Psycho-religious healing brings the troubled soul into harmony with self, with fellowman, and with God, thus ending the conflicts and disorders of body and soul.

"VIS MEDICATRIX DEI"

Of course, we do not mean by psycho-religious healing that it is the religious counsellor who does the healing; all the healer, whoever he may be, can do is to remove the obstacles to the natural healing powers resident in us. This "vis medicatrix naturae," healing power of nature, is what cures, whatever may be the technique, whether by drugs, by surgery, by physiotherapy, by psychoanalysis, by suggestion, by hypnosis, by reëducation, by prayer, by laying on of hands, by anointing.

But I think we are right in seeing this as God's activity. He is working not only in the unusual, startling, or miraculous; just as truly He is working in the regular, orderly processes of nature. We might better say "vis medicatrix Dei," the healing power of God—as does Dr. Cabot.[6] His working is seen in the "spiritual work" of the church and its workers; and it is no less present in the scientific discoveries and skills of medicine, surgery, and psychology. Wise medical men still know that old Ambroise Paré was right in his oft-repeated phrase, "I dressed him, God healed him." All healing is of God; and God is on the side of health, ever working for the health of body and psyche.

Psychotherapy may remove some of the things that block the healing power of nature, of God: it may take away morbid fears, anxieties, conflicts of instincts and emotions, the resentments and hates, and the guilt-feelings of the patient, by making him aware of the origin of his ills, by helping him to achieve a right insight. But this may fail to heal. There is an additional restorative power in religion that psychotherapy, as such, does not have. Hadfield, a leading British psychiatrist, says, "The Christian religion is one of the most valuable and potent influences that we possess for producing that harmony and peace of mind and that confidence of soul which is needed to bring health and power to a large proportion of nervous patients. In some cases I have attempted to cure nervous patients with suggestions of quietness and confidence, but without success until I have linked these suggestions on to that faith in the power of God which is the substance of the Christian's confidence and hope." [7]

I have already spoken of the importance of the "will to live"

[6] Richard C. Cabot and Russell L. Dicks, *The Art of Ministering to the Sick,* pp. 118 f. (Macmillan Co., New York, 1936).

[7] J. A. Hadfield, "The Psychology of Power," in *The Spirit,* by B. H. Streeter and others, pp. 110–111 (Macmillan Co., New York, 1919).

in the sick person. Many seriously ill go on to recovery even when the odds are against them; others lacking this "will to live," even though less critically ill, go on to die, in spite of the best treatment. Of course, this is not just "will-power"; there is will and emotion united in a passion to go on living for some-one, for something—it may be the love of a mother for her children that will not let her die and leave them, or the devotion of a man to his family, love that conquers death. Can we doubt that religion adds to the devotion and joy of living?

It was a religious motive that gave the will to live in a woman told about by Stanley Jones. A mother had died of tuberculosis and left six small children; her sister took over the care of the children, but she too caught the infection and was given no chance to live by her doctors. This was back in the days before medical science had learned so much about what can be done for tuberculosis. She was expected to die, but she lived and cared for the children of her sister; she had made this her life work, and live she would. Each day she had one of the children stand in the corner away from her, but so she could see the child; she would say to herself, "I must live to raise this family!" And live she did; and she raised the family. Dr. Jones calls her one of the most radiant and useful persons he knows.[8]

Sometimes, nothing can overcome the disease; but even so the will to live is important for recovery, to take advantage of every chance for life. We may see Jesus' recognition of this fact in the question he asked of the man at the pool of Bethesda, thirty-eight years an invalid, "Wilt thou be made whole?" I like the Revised Standard Version, "Do you want to be healed?" May we also see in this a recognition of the fact that

[8] Jones, *op. cit.*, p. 75.

nature and God are on the side of healing? That it is the "vis medicatrix Dei" that heals? I truly believe this.

RELIGIOUS PSYCHOTHERAPY

There are ills that can be healed only by spiritual means, by religious psychotherapy or psycho-religious therapy; they are of spiritual origin, conflicts in the spirit, with physical effects. The sufferer in such cases will probably not be able to find his way to relief, without help from some wise counsellor or therapist. A physician or psychiatrist must use spiritual or religious ideas to help these people, or fail in his therapy; or he may send his patient to someone who will use religious therapy.

Alvarez tells of a woman who came to him with one of the worst neuroses he remembers; during the financial crash of 1931, her father had taken all her money trying to stop a run on his bank—and lost it all. She became so enraged she gave him a tongue-lashing: his answer was to go to his room and blow out his brains; but he left a note saying that he was paying back her money in the only way he could—with his life insurance. She went to pieces nervously and physically, conscience-stricken. Alvarez added that "naturally there wasn't much that I could do to help her." [9] Surely, this was a case for psycho-religious healing, or at least for spiritual counselling; but no record is made of any being offered to her.

Not infrequently I tell patients who consult me in the clinic that medicines will not do them any good, that they need real religion. One of these was a man who had a variety of complaints, nervous and digestive; as I talked to him, I asked him

[9] Walter C. Alvarez, *Nervousness, Indigestion, and Pain*, p. 286 (Paul B. Hoeber, New York, 1943).

whether he attended church and had a religious experience; he
told me he was a deacon in his church, but was not getting much
joy out of his religion. He confessed to fears, and when asked
more about this, he said he was afraid to die; he felt a weight
of guilt and was not ready to face God. I asked him if he did
not believe God was willing to forgive; he said that he had
prayed for forgiveness, but that he was still afraid. I told him I
would not give him any medicine; that what he needed was to
take God at His word, and thank Him for His love and accept
the forgiveness the Lord freely gives—he was content to go
with that treatment.

Weatherhead tells of a young woman who came to consult
him, suffering from headaches, catarrh, and insomnia; she had
been under doctors' care and had taken bottles and bottles of
medicines; but got no better. It came out that six or seven years
earlier she had been wronged by a friend; while her good sense
counselled forgiveness and reconciliation, her resentment, plus
a terrible opportunity for revenge, impelled her towards retalia-
tion. She was desperately struggling and suffering, spiritually
and physically. She was helped to do the Christian thing, to
seek out her friend and forgive and be reconciled; she did this
and in a few days came back cured and radiant; and she stayed
well. Her physical ills were due directly to her bitter, hostile
spirit: religion is *the* cure for such.[10]

Kemp quotes two doctors reporting on a study of rheumatoid arthritis: they found an astonishing number of their patients were "fearfully facing life's responsibilities." They said
that the "solution begins in an honest facing of themselves with
the doctor and, with his aid, ends in the development of a vital
faith. A deep religious faith is the most effective faith, provided

[10] Leslie Weatherhead, *Psychology in Service of the Soul*, p. 10 (Macmillan
Co., New York, 1930).

the doctor himself has such a faith to give. Five years of observation has convinced us that just facing these negative attitudes is not enough to overcome them, but with the development of a faith, fear goes, improved health follows, and most important of all for the future of the patient, personality changes take place. . . . We are convinced that the control of the psychogenic factors in chronic rheumatoid arthritis lies in the development of a vital faith, which will meet these needs with its positive philosophy of living." [11]

Yet we must also point out that many sick people are not interested in religion; they are so indifferent that religion would have little value for them. I seriously question whether the figures given by Dr. G. Canby Robinson are representative of the common run of people: he made a study of 174 cases in Johns Hopkins Hospital, and found only 7 cases in which he thought religion would be a help. I am sure a larger proportion of sick people would welcome and profit by religious help in their times of sickness. But he is right in saying that "the general indifference of the patients toward religion created a barrier between them and the spiritual and social services which the church could render." [12] And this barrier may be broken down by wise, tactful spiritual helpfulness. The case of the "scientific agnostic" who talked to Dr. Worcester and was healed, is an illustration of this; religion overcame the barriers.

Very often the medical men either do not seek, or fail to find the spiritual disorder that is behind the physical symptoms and signs. A woman came to Weatherhead from a long distance, after having had treatments from medical specialists, and finding no relief. She was unable to sleep, and feared that

[11] George W. Gray, *The Advancing Front of Medicine*, p. 229 (McGraw-Hill Book Co., New York—copyright, 1941, by George Gray).

[12] G. Canby Robinson, *The Patient as a Person*, pp. 39-40 (Commonwealth Fund, New York, 1939—permission of the publisher).

in her utter hopelessness she might take her own life. In the course of her interviews with Dr. Weatherhead, it came out that she had done something she thought could never be forgiven. It took many hours to get her to accept the idea of the forgiveness of God and believe that He would put our sins behind His back forever. The next thing was to get her to accept the idea that God had a purpose for her life in the future, that His grace would be sufficient for the day, day by day. She did accept this religious faith, and gained physical strength, and her facial expression was altered.[13] The physicians who had treated her had not found the spiritual disorder—they were not looking for unforgiven sins. Religion is *the* cure for such.

I want now to take up some of the specific emotions that need religion for their best treatment and for complete relief from the illness resulting from the wrong emotions. Guilt definitely needs religion for its therapy; anger and hostility belong to another group; anxiety, in all its forms, is another. Let us take them up in order:

GUILT AND FORGIVENESS

It is the feeling of guilt, rather than the fact of wrongdoing, that brings on illness; so there may be cases in which the guilt feeling is a great factor in an illness, but in which there is little or no real guilt; a morbid conscience may accuse the sufferer of wrongdoing of which he is really innocent. Children may suffer greatly from a feeling of guilt because of hostility toward a parent who has been unfair or unloving, but here the real culprit is the father or mother who gave the child a basis for his hostile feelings. And of course a mother who never wanted or loved her child has a reason for guilty feelings. But there

[13] Weatherhead, *op. cit.*, p. 75.

are plenty of things done that are wrong and for which one ought to feel guilt and shame.

Guilt and anxiety can wreak dire consequences on persons who have tender consciences; this is well illustrated by a story told by Dr. Peale. He was visited by a little white-haired lady, obviously in great distress. She told him of years of suffering from a sense of guilt; but she reminded him of Whistler's portrait of his mother, and he could hardly believe that she could be suffering from guilt. Her story was that when a girl of eighteen years, she had been very much in love with a young man who was more loose in his ideas about personal purity; he tried to persuade her that it was no sin to violate the strict sex code she had always held, and she was tempted. She was so much in love that it took "an awful battle with myself to resist it." She did not yield; but she felt guilty because of her desire. She had suffered from this guilt feeling for more than fifty years; though she had not sinned, and had instead won a fine victory over sin. Of course Dr. Peale was able by religious counsel to relieve her and give her peace and joy.[14]

Another more complicated case of guilt feeling is told by Dunbar: it was a young woman in a hospital suffering from diabetes, with a tendency to go into shock after her doses of insulin. This case was what Dunbar calls a "delayed-action mine of childhood," a victim of an unwise parent. As far back as she could remember, she had been told by her father that her birth had been the cause of her mother's insanity, and the father seemed to consider this her fault and accept no share himself. The mother was cared for in the home till she tried to poison herself and the child; the little girl ran to the nurse and

[14] Norman Vincent Peale, *A Guide to Confident Living*, pp. 43 f. (Prentice-Hall, New York, 1948).

both mother and child were saved by stomach-pumps. After the mother was sent to an institution for mental cases, every time the girl was taken to see her she had a convulsion. The doctor finally ordered that she be no more taken to see her mother. Then the guardian to whom she was turned over, treated her so cruelly that she ran away as soon as she was old enough to get a job. She did well as a sales-girl and worked up to become a buyer for a gift shop. She was married at twenty-four, but continued to work. After twelve years, she again went to see her mother, probably from a sense of duty; within a short time she was in the hospital with diabetes. The "delayed-action mine of childhood" had exploded and caused her sickness. Dunbar says that superficial psychotherapy helped her gain insight, and she was freed of the guilt feeling and recovered from her illness.[15] I do not know whether religious ideas were used in this case—they might very properly have been. This truly seems to have been a case where religious counselling would have been a real help.

It takes more than just uncovering the guilt as the psychogenic factor in the illness; there needs to be forgiveness and assurance of it; and in any case where there is real guilt, it takes more than self-forgiveness. Where a sane view reveals no real guilt, insight may be enough; but this is not so in cases where the guilt feeling is based on wrongdoing. Sometimes the sufferer well knows wherein he is guilty, he knows his sin; but too often the guilt has been repressed, the sin not confessed even to one's self. It takes confession and, so far as can be, righting the wrongs done; forgiveness and reconciliation are needed in such cases; and for a real cure of guilt a hope of

[15] Flanders Dunbar, *Mind and Body: Psychosomatic Medicine*, pp. 20 f. (Random House, New York, 1947).

redemption is essential. Religion offers not only forgiveness of sins done, but also a new work of God in the inner spirit to overcome the evil, a work of the Holy Spirit in the subconscious depths of being, transforming the nature of the guilty person.

Guilt may be a factor in illness even in folk who deny any sense of sin or wrongdoing. This is shown in the case of a young officer in the Air Force who was shot down while on a mission during the late war. He escaped and was taken to a hospital, where he received the best of treatment; but he did not recover. The doctor turned him over to the chaplain, and he was introduced to a minister-counsellor. During the interviews, it came out that before going to the front he committed a sex sin: he rationalized it on the basis that he was going away and might never return, and anyway he and the girl hoped they might be married later. Both of them had changed their minds and were no longer interested in each other. His conscious mind rationalized and excused his conduct, and he did not feel that what he had done was really wrong, as the social set he ran with thought they were free from the old ideas of sin, and that the common practice of such things by his associates freed him from any sense of shame about it. But in spite of his mental subterfuges, his subconscious mind told him he had done what was wrong and that he was guilty, and this made him truly ill. He tried to cover his sense of guilt and it festered. When he was willing to get his sins forgiven, he was greatly changed; he became free, happy, and full of energy, and finally regained his health. When discharged from the service, he found a good job, and has been very successful. Peale says that this young man had thought himself emancipated from old-fashioned moral standards; but nineteen hundred years of Christian civilization had made his subconscious mind know that it was wrong.[16] We may see in this some of the basis for Jung's postulate of a "collective unconscious." In any case it required religion to restore this young man to health; he found the "Healer who keeps office in the New Testament."

It is needless to say that some people commit heinous sins, and yet do not have psychosomatic illnesses; while others whose sins are generally considered peccadilloes become seriously ill. It is not the wrongdoing or the sin, but the feeling of guilt, the emotion, that brings on the sickness; some folk seem to be too hardened to habitual sinning to have any sense of guilt; some hold to such low moral standards that they feel no guilt—in the conscious mind, at least. And the common indifference toward any thought of God, the secularism of so many people, leaves little reason for any sense of sin and guilt, even a feeling of shame for wrongs done to their fellows; yet even these are sometimes unable to get away from self-condemnation.

The sense of guilt may be due to a great variety of causes: children often feel guilt because of disobedience toward a parent, or because of lack of love, when the fault is really that of the parent in treating the child unfairly or harshly, or in failing to give the child the love he craves; or it may be because of too great possessiveness and not giving the child his natural opportunity to mature. There are wrongs we have done to others that make us feel guilty; and at times when we have suffered wrongs at the hands of others, our reactions may cause us to be ashamed of ourselves and feel guilty. Violations of law, betrayals of trust, easily result in an uneasy conscience. But probably the most frequent cause of guilt feeling is some

[16] Peale, *op. cit.*, pp. 39 f.

form of the sex act. Sadler reports that he found about fifty percent of his cases had a sex problem; [17] so naturally guilt over sex is a major psychogenic factor in illness.

For the sin-sick soul, sick because of its guilt and fears and anxiety, of course, medicines and rest-cures are inadequate; scientific psychotherapy without the use of religion cannot truly heal these souls. For such as these only genuine religion, a real experience of the power of God can suffice; for no forgiveness so deeply affects the whole being as does His; and no other power can reach down into the very depths of the personality and change it into a new creature by His Spirit's working.

For these guilty souls, religion naturally emphasizes the love and forgiveness of God, and His power to help us in a new life. "For Thou, Lord, art good, and ready to forgive, and abundant in loving kindness unto all them that call on Thee." "Thus saith the high and lofty One that inhabiteth eternity, I dwell in the high and holy place, with him also that is of a contrite and humble spirit, to revive the heart of the contrite." "God so loved the world that He gave His Son that whosoever believeth in Him should not perish." "If we confess our sins, He is faithful and righteous to forgive us our sins, and to cleanse us from all unrighteousness." [18]

This divine forgiveness is basic in psycho-religious healing. But it is not all that is involved in forgiveness: there must be in ourselves a forgiving spirit; we must be reconciled to our brother, even before we dare present ourselves in worship: "Forgive us as we forgive." We need to get the forgiveness of our brother for the wrongs we have done to him; if we are not

[17] William S. Sadler, *The Mind at Mischief*, p. 108 (Funk & Wagnalls Co., New York, 1929).
[18] Psalm 86:5; Isaiah 57:15; John 3:16; I John 1:9.

willing to make things right so far as possible, we have no right to ask God to forgive us. This may lead to some real problems as to whether we may not possibly do as much or more harm by confession, in some cases, than would be done by letting the past die. I believe no rule can apply to all cases: each must be decided on its own merits. But I am sure that confession and restitution are imperative sometimes. Religion is not just between a man and his God; right religion involves right relations with his brother man. A religious counsellor may be of great help to the guilty soul in this, helping him to find out his guilt and sin and to turn to God for forgiveness. It takes more than insight as to the nature of the illness; it takes appropriate follow-up, carrying through in right living with our fellow men and in the sight of God.

There is also a still further benefit offered by religion in the cure of guilt: God offers His own Spirit to come into our hearts and make changes in our very selves. Not that He promises to make us perfect so we can no longer wrong anyone or offend in His sight; but He does promise to make new creatures of us, to work in us and give us new power. "If a man love me he will keep my word, and my Father will love him, and we will come unto him and make our abode with him." "It is no longer I that live, but Christ liveth in me." "The Spirit of God dwelleth in you." "I am with you always, even unto the end of the world." [19]

ANGER, RESENTMENT, HATE

Anger has been called one of the major sins, according to the psychologist (Ligon [20]); fear is the other—and guilt is com-

---

[19] John 14:23; Gal. 2:20; I Cor. 3:16; Mat. 28:20.
[20] Ernest M. Ligon, *Psychology of Christian Personality*, p. 16 (Macmillan Co., New York, 1935).

monly associated with them. Whether we look on them as sins or not, we know they are major factors in psychogenic illnesses. We have seen how anger affects the sympathetic nervous system and may produce actual physical illness. The small child who gives way to a temper tantrum is likely to have a gastric upset. Adults frequently note that headaches often follow anger, especially repressed temper. We have cited instances of hostility, resentment, and hate as causes of prolonged and serious physical disease. These serious ills come, not from the passing anger, but from the continued hostile feelings, the resentments, the grudges, the hates, that embitter the spirit.

These psychic factors in sickness may be repressed and totally unconscious to the patient, or they may be known and recognized as disturbing things in his life, but not felt to have any connection with his illness; but many people know their temper has a lot to do with their symptoms. Probably in most cases there is some repression of the hostile feelings.

It seldom goes so far, but Alvarez tells of a man who killed himself by hostile feelings. He had been in good health up to the time he became enraged over a lawsuit brought against him by a sister. It obsessed him, he could think or talk of nothing else. His breath became foul and stayed so; his appetite failed; his digestion grew bad; he lost sleep; his weight dropped away. Then his heart and kidneys began to fail; and before many months he was dead. Alvarez says, "It seemed obvious that he died from bodily injuries wrought by powerful emotion." [21]

Dunbar tells of another whose repressed anger and resentment finally caused his death. As a youth he got along so badly with his step-father that he ran away from home; he violently objected to the third marriage of his mother after the death of her second husband; he did not have a satisfactory home of

[21] Alvarez, *op. cit.*, p. 20.

his own when he married; his relations with his wife were cold; he had to have a business partner, and continually resented this loss of freedom, and became quite irritable. Yet he repressed his anger, and went on till he had several coronary episodes, and finally was sent to the hospital for treatment. After a short stay in the hospital, he went home; but within the year he was back again and died in an oxygen tent. Dunbar points out that he did not understand his emotional conflict, resentment, and suppressed aggression.[22] Psychotherapy was inadequate in this case: though other patients do gain a proper insight as to their emotions and make good adjustments and recover. I was reading a medical article recently, in which this fact of the importance of emotional control was stressed. The writer said that for heart disease patients "the achievement of complete emotional adjustment and the studied cultivation of a maximal degree of serenity" is essential for well-being; the "curbing of the emotions" is mandatory in protective living in heart cases.[23]

It seems to me quite evident that a genuine religious experience would help such patients to overcome their angers and resentments. The cure is not by repression, but by "the expulsive power of a new affection," Christian love. Hostility and hatred must be ended by a forgiving spirit; and truly religion helps in the attainment of this. The cure for all forms of hostile feelings and emotions is love. One wishes we had a new word for it; the word "love" has been soiled by ill-usage. The kind of love that cures these ill-humors is not erotic love—this may be a part of the problem; it is more than an emotional attraction to one of the opposite sex, or of the same sex as in friendship; it is not the possessive love of parent or

---

[22] Dunbar, *op. cit.*, pp. 119–122.

[23] O. P. J. Falk, "Are Cardiac Deaths Ever Preventable?" *Annals of Western Medicine and Surgery*, Vol. 5, pp. 121–124 (Feb., 1951).

friend; it is rather that which seeks ever the good of the loved one; it has been called "unfailing goodwill," such as fatherly love is at its best, and the self-giving love of a mother. Ligon properly says that it is more than "brotherly love"; [24] only the completely unselfish love of a father, mother, or friend comes up to the ideal of Christian love.

Yet as I have looked through medical and religious literature on this theme, I have found few references to the use of religion in the cure of illness due to anger and hostility, grudges and resentments, ill-will. Of course common sense will enable many to see the folly of continued hostility, when a counsellor—or self-study—has helped one to gain insight as to what these feelings are doing to his life. This ethical or practical therapy accounts for good results in many cases of illness and malad-justment. Dunbar illustrates this in one of her case histories: a diabetic woman had suffered for seven years, not only from the diabetes but also from severe neuritic pains, from cardiac pains, from headaches and dizziness, from numbness, and from obesity. She herself had found that annoyance and rage caused her more trouble than potatoes, candy, or ice cream. In the first interview she relieved herself of much pent-up grievance; she coöperated with the psychiatrist and gained insight as to her emotional and personality difficulties; she got relief from her various pains, and her diabetes improved markedly. [25] Dr. Dunbar makes no mention of the use of religious principles, of "psycho-religious therapy" in this case; but I suspect that they were part of the "superficial psychotherapy" she says she used. Anyhow, it seems to me that the use of religion, definite religious teachings, would be a real help toward the relief of such people.

[24] Ligon, *op. cit.*, p. 63.
[25] Dunbar, *op. cit.*, p. 61.

Frequent, persistent colds have been attributed to anger and resentments, and relieved when the cause of the anger has been removed, or insight as to what it was doing has been achieved. Asthma is sometimes blamed on repressed hostility, and relieved by getting rid of the hostility. (Of course, I am not suggesting that even the majority of such cases are due to this cause.) Some patients confess that it is a relief to have a cardiac pain to fight instead of a husband or other close relative; hostile feelings toward mothers-in-law aggravate many psychosomatic ills; bitterness toward hard parents, or toward brothers or sisters, is a common item in case histories; and when the hostile feelings are overcome or removed, definite relief follows. This common-sense treatment of hostility or resentment makes no pretense to being religious; yet it seems to me that there is more religion in it than we think: it is practical religion to forgive and throw off our grudges and hates. But why should not frank religious appeals be made to forgive, and to love? Surely, the forgiving love of God is the best and most permanent basis for human forgiveness anyone could have. "Forgive us as we forgive."

Another reason for appeal to religious ideas is found in the fact that often the bitterness and hostility shown toward others is due to dissatisfaction with one's own self, is a manifestation of dislike of self, a guilt feeling. Bonnell illustrates this in a story of a teacher who confessed that she was terribly lonely, and had not a friend left; she was having trouble with everybody and was bitter toward all. He let her tell her story; then he asked, "Why do you hate yourself so much?" She was surprised at that: he explained that her bitterness toward others was hatred of herself projected onto others. She confessed that she hated herself, but protested that she had never realized she was turning it onto others. The confession of guilt over an affair with a married man followed; when she was led to accept the forgiveness of God, and His willingness to enable her to live a new life, she could smile again.[26]

Much of the hostilities we feel are really ingrown self-esteem: we resent what others do to us because we are thinking of self so much; even things that do not affect us we resent because we are jealous and want to get recognition for ourselves. Sometimes we feel the success of another is an affront—though we would not admit it. An appeal to religious ideas helps turn our thinking from self to God; this helps us to get away from the ill-feelings, for the things that arouse bad feelings in us do not count for so much when God is in our thought, we see them more nearly as they appear to Him.

Beyond this common-sense psychotherapy of hostility, there is a curative power in religion—though, as we have said, there may be religion in practice even if not avowed, in the ordinary therapy. The cure for anger, hate, grudges, resentment, all forms of hostility, is in forgiveness and love, rather than just in passing them by or letting them go. Unlovely emotions can be overcome by the expulsive power of a new affection, love. Only a genuine religious experience can enable you to "love your enemies, pray for them that despitefully use you, and do good to them that hate you." Only religion can put a spirit in us that will "forgive until seventy times seven." "God is love," and anyone who genuinely loves his neighbor is religious, even though he may make no profession. "Love suffereth long and is kind. . . . beareth all things, believeth all things, hopeth all things, endureth all things. Love never faileth." And religion

[26] John G. Bonnell, *Pastoral Psychiatry*, pp. 62–65 (Harper & Brothers, New York, 1938).

is the great source of this love, this unfailing goodwill; the love of God shed abroad in our hearts by His Spirit enables us so to love that these unlovely passions and emotions lose their power over us.

Religion gives many illustrations of this power of love to overcome hate and hostility: such as that Christian love of an Armenian nurse who forgave and nursed back to health the Turk she had seen brutally kill her brother. When wounded and desperately sick, he was brought to the hospital and put under her care, she knew him and, overcoming hate, by Christian care she led him to express a desire to become a Christian.

It was religion that moved a Korean pastor to ask the court to entrust to his care a young communist, condemned to death by the court for the brutal murder of the two sons of the pastor. The murderer was little more than a lad, but a convinced and heartless communist. The pastor's sons had been students and Christian leaders in their school; captured by communists, they gave their Christian witness, and both were cruelly put to death. The pastor got the consent of the court, and took this young man into his home in place of the sons he had lost. Religion has put this spirit into many who have suffered less grievously than this Korean Christian. What a power for the cure of hate! And how sadly it is neglected!

FEAR, ANXIETY, WORRY

Sadler well says, "Fear is the psychological signal to the sympathetic nervous system to step on the physiologic accelerator, the adrenal gland." [27] This is a concise summary of the effects of fear on the nervous system; we have already given illustrations of the effects on the body of fear, and anxiety, and

[27] Sadler, *op. cit.*, p. 124.

worry, and how they produce actual physical disease. Fears and worries are generally attached to things external, things that may happen to us: such as worry about finances and jobs, about security, about family, about sickness or injury, and about death. A great deal of this is worry about things that never occur. Anxieties generally center about self, and may come from a sense of inadequacy or an inferiority feeling; they may go on into a neurosis, "anxiety neurosis," with many physical symptoms along with the mental.

Many of these anxieties and worries have their origin in childhood experiences: a child may feel unwanted and unloved, or may be mistreated; this gives a deep anxiety, a feeling of insecurity. The child may be mistaken about the lack of love: but it is his emotions that count, not what the parent actually does. Probably this is a factor in delinquency, and in psychosomatic ills among children of broken homes. Whatever makes children feel inferior and inadequate renders them vulnerable to anxiety ills in later years.

It seems that some people are the "worrying kind"; they are more liable to worry and anxiety illness than the more healthy-minded. These folk appear to have a store of suppressed or repressed anxieties, probably subconscious; then comes some situation or condition of difficulty, financial reverses, loss of job, ill health of self or of someone in the family, or actual danger. The "old morbid anxieties attach themselves to objective fears" and troubles ensue.

The anxieties appear quite reasonable to the patient, even when others see their foolishness; our own fears are all quite reasonable to ourselves. Blanton tells of a man of seventy-five, with investments amounting to hundreds of thousands of dollars, worrying for fear inflation or a capital levy would leave him "poverty-stricken in my old age"; he could not see that most of his old age was already gone.[28]

Probably guilt feelings as a cause of anxiety should have more illustrations: Blanton tells of a middle-aged woman caring for her eighty-year-old father, a cantankerous, dominating, domineering old man—as he had always been. He had refused to hire a nurse to care for him, insisting that the daughter do it; he was as unthoughtful of her welfare in his sickness as he had been when she gave up the young man she loved to wait on him. She would become panic-stricken when away from him for a while and would hurry home to see that he was not dead. Her anxiety grew so she would hardly leave the house. But Blanton pointed out to her that her anxiety about her father was really a subconscious antagonism and hate because of what he had done to her life. But she repressed such thoughts, and felt guilty over even thinking them.[29] He tells of another young woman who professed to be seriously concerned about the impending divorce and remarriage of her brother; in truth her anxiety was because she had fallen in love with her employer, and they had talked about his getting a divorce to marry her—but she would not consent to that. She came to see that her anxiety was really about herself.[30]

Of course ordinary psychotherapy clears up many of these fears, anxieties, and worries. Some of them are so unreasonable that bringing them to the light robs them of all power to harm, when faced up to with appropriate action. Insight may be enough to overcome some of them; but often it is only religious faith that is adequate, as Hadfield says in the sentence already quoted, "In some cases I have attempted to cure nervous patients with suggestions of quietness and confidence, but without success until I have linked these suggestions on to that faith in the power of God which is the substance of the Christian's confidence." It takes more than just a philosophy of life, as a man who had been through a very serious operation, and peered out through a mass of bandages, said, "Since I came to this hospital I have made a discovery that I shall not forget as long as I live. It is this: when a man comes up against the real issues of life and death, he needs something more than a philosophy of life—he needs a faith." [31]

Faith and hope are *the* cure for fear, worry, and anxiety. Faith in self, faith in our fellowmen, faith in God: these are what the anxious spirit needs. Religious faith gives more power to overcome than can psychology or psychiatry; it puts faith on the sound basis of God's power and goodness, His fatherhood. "Faith is the Answer." Faith in God helps when the situation is truly most hard and difficult—almost hopeless. Peale gives a story of a man who was helped only when religion was applied to his case. He was a leading figure on Wall Street—life was like a song; until the crash came in 1929. He lost everything he owned, even his home; then his wife died; and as a climax he took encephalitis, sleeping-sickness or brain fever. The doctors said he made a good recovery for one who had had such a disease; but he went from neurologist to neurologist, from osteopath to osteopath, from diet faddist to diet faddist—and lost in weight and gained in irritability. He became a neurotic and hypochondriac, a trial to family, to friends, and to self; he even contemplated suicide to end it all. Then one day he met a man whose office was in the same building as his; this friend urged him to put his trust in God, to quit worrying about

[31] Bonnell, *op. cit.*, p. 92.

self. Self-pity, ill-will, and fears were put out of his heart; he learned to read the Bible and to pray, to live as in the presence of God. He became a new man physically, and again a success in his business, and particularly in his spirit. He met one of the doctors from the psychiatry clinic he had attended, and told the doctor of his recovery. The doctor remarked, "We work along the same lines, except for excluding the religious element." "Yes, that's what's the trouble," he replied. "It was not until I found the religious element that anything happened to me." [32] Psychiatry failed to cure this man; but religious faith did.

I cannot believe that faith is a cure for all ills: it cannot keep death away forever, all of us must die sometime. And many folk must hold onto faith even in the midst of prolonged suffering and in serious losses. Religion does not assure freedom from troubles and pain or death, but it does enable us to overcome fear. This is well expressed by MacMurray: "To the man who is afraid of poverty, it does not say, 'God will save you from losing your money.' It says, 'Suppose you do lose your money, what is there to be afraid of in that?' If it is fear of suffering and death that haunts you, real religion says, 'Yes, of course, you will suffer and of course you will die, but there is nothing to be afraid of in that!' . . . True religion says, 'Look the facts that you are afraid of in the face; see them in all their brutality and ugliness; and you will find, not that they are unreal, but that they are not to be feared.' " [33]

Religious faith sings, "Though I walk through the valley of the shadow of death, I will fear no evil; for Thou art with me." God is with the trusting soul; and God cares: then fear

[32] Peale, *A Guide to Confident Living*, pp. 109 ff. (Prentice-Hall, 1948).
[33] John MacMurray, *Freedom in the Modern World*, p. 59 (Faber & Faber, London, 1932—permission of the publishers).

not! Faith says with Paul, "In everything God works for good with those who love Him." Faith in God gives meaning to life, and takes away fear of death. "The fear of civilized man is himself," says Hadfield. Man needs to turn from self to God in faith; and fears and anxieties will go—regardless of his situation, and whatever the end. The fears and anxieties that afflict us, such as fear of unpopularity, fear of being a failure, fear of people, fear of unemployment, fear of poverty, fear of loneliness, fear of the dark, fear of illness, fear of death—all our fears and anxieties will yield to faith, when the faith is in God. Not that we will not have to endure some of these things and finally face death itself, but that the fear will be overcome. "Thou wilt keep him in perfect peace, whose mind is stayed on Thee; because he trusteth in Thee." *Faith is the answer!*

PRAYERS FOR AND WITH THE SICK

I have little patience with those who think that if they use religious means to help the sick, there must not be any use of medicines or anything else doctors may do for the sick. Religion can be an aid to healing while we are using the best that medical science can offer. We do not need to give up what God gives us through science just because we pray for the sick. We may rightly pray for the doctors and nurses, that they may be given the wisdom and strength to do the right thing for their patients. And we may also pray for the healing power that God alone can give. Many of my friends have been convinced that prayers for their recovery and for recovery of loved ones, have been a real power for healing in desperate illness—and they also fully appreciate the work of doctors and nurses. Physicians and surgeons often add prayer to their labors for the sick; and some freely acknowledge that without prayer some of their recovered patients would not be living. Many of my friends attribute their present health to unceasing prayer and faith. I realize that there is no way to prove this: others have not been spared for whom just as earnest prayers have been made. But when one has seen it on the mission field and in the homeland through the years, he comes to feel that there is healing power in prayer and faith, even though he cannot prove it, and in spite of unanswered prayers.

I believe that prayers for, and *with* the sick have power. All doctors know and acknowledge the power of the will to live, and prayer gives religious reinforcement to the will to live in the sick person. The power of suggestion is recognized: what better suggestion could there be than prayer with the sick? Thoughts are powerful things: it seems to me reasonable to expect that thoughts of recovery and health expressed in prayer should have real physical effects for good. I have many times prayed with the sick, prayed for recovery and health—but always with the further prayer implied if not expressed, that if healing were not to be, that God's comforting and sustaining presence should be made real to the sick person, whatever might be the end. And I have seen patients helped to suffer and hold fast to faith in the goodness and love of God; some have gone through the valley of death—not just the "shadow" of it—in peace and joy. In all our prayers for recovery and health, we have to keep in mind that sometimes the answer of God is "My grace is sufficient for thee," so that even a thorn in the flesh can be borne gladly. Of course we must all suffer and finally die, but God gives victory over the fear and sting of death, when He cannot give healing and health.

Again I want to emphasize that I am convinced that there is power for healing as well as for comfort in the prayer of faith. This is more than psychotherapy, more than just suggestion, more than the power of thought and attention, of emotion; it is opening the whole being, body and soul, to the all-pervasive power of God, and there is healing in this—"vis medicatrix Dei." Not that all will be healed, but that more will be, than if prayer and faith in God be not used; that many will find health restored when they are spiritually right with God and with their fellowmen. So much of our illness has a spiritual element in its causation, that we ought to expect that getting spiritually right would help in the cure of sickness. Stanley Jones quotes a doctor as saying, "If three-quarters of my patients found God they would be well." [34] He may have estimated the percentage too high; but there is truth in what he says. Can we doubt that the prayers of the sick, for the sick, and with the sick, will help them find God? And finding Him, their guilt, sins, fears, anxieties, worries, griefs, hates, and hostilities, all are relieved; peace, joy, and love are bestowed upon them from God, and these are healing. Dare we set a limit to the power of God to heal? "Have faith in God."

In this discussion we have tried to show how religion can be a real help in healing and for health; as for techniques, how one can avail himself of the resources of religion, our next chapter will be given to that, but mainly as to how we can use religion to achieve and maintain health rather than in the cure of illness. I believe the sick person should seek aid from medical men to make sure there is no serious physical disease, and from religious counsellors for the help religion can give.

[34] Jones, *op. cit.*, p. 167.

VI

Religion and Healthy Living

RELIGION IS NO GUARANTEE of a healthy body; but it should help us to make and keep our bodies more fit than they otherwise would be. Just as psychologists, according to Link,[1] found that religious people have better personalities, they ought to be more healthy. And I believe that religion has resources for healthy living, as well as curative power; it is of value for prevention as well as for the treatment of illness. In this chapter, I want to point out some of the ways that it can be a help to us in daily living, in making life better.

Religion must not be an excuse for neglect or violation of the laws of hygiene and sanitation; we have no right to expect the Lord to give us good health if we disobey the laws He has ordained. Piety is no substitute for sanity or hygiene. There is no saintliness in failing to take proper care of our bodies. True religion ought to give us a keener conscience to follow the rules of health, the laws of God for our good. It is our religious duty to be as healthy as we can, for these bodies of ours are to be "temples." "Glorify God in your body."

Religion promotes good health for individuals, and it fosters hygiene and public health activities for better common welfare. It seems more than coincidence that it is in lands where the highest forms of religion prevail that we find the best health, the

[1] Henry C. Link, *The Return to Religion*, p. 13 (Macmillan Co., New York, 1936).

lowest morbidity and mortality rates. Infant and child mortality rates are about the best indices of public health; the lowest rates, the best, are found in countries where high religion prevails; the worst mortality rates are in lands where religion is degraded.

When previously healthy persons find either mental or physical well-being sinking below par, it is the proper thing to have a physical examination by a qualified doctor; and when psychic or moral problems are involved, one should see a wise counsellor. It is sane advice: "Do not keep your troubles to yourself." But here we are concerned with the ways in which religion can help us in daily normal living, ways in which we can use religion to promote our physical and spiritual well-being, health.

1. *Honest Work:* There is a health value in honest work, and true religion inculcates this virtue. When Captain John Smith ruled that the settlers in the colony at Jamestown must work or not eat, he was but applying a verse from the Bible: "If any man will not work, neither let him eat" (2 Thess. 3:10). And of course this goes back to the Ten Commandments: "Six days shalt thou labor." There is a satisfaction in good honest work; and satisfaction promotes a healthy nervous system—to say nothing about a good digestion. I am sure all of us have known people who complain of many ills while we know they would be better physically and spiritually if they would go to work. The body rests better after work.

This does not mean that religion encourages work that has become drudgery; and most assuredly it does not mean that religion favors the exploitation of the worker—in spite of the fact that some divines can be quoted as saying that hard labor and poverty are good for common people. This is not the voice of the Church. Work can become so hard it hurts the man; it can degrade when the laborer becomes just "The Man with the Hoe." Religion approves and encourages work that is honorable and for the good of man. And I think we may rightly claim that religion has done much to lift the burden of degrading labor and drudgery from the backs of men; it has been a pioneer in striving for better working conditions and for the right of labor to share justly in the products of his toil. I believe the idea of the "brotherhood of man under the Fatherhood of God" has been the great emancipator of slaves, and has made work an honor and a good instead of a curse.

We often hear that "it is not work but worry that kills," but work done under too great tension and strain and too long continued, work while feeling unjustly treated, these may be just as killing as worry, they produce undue fatigue which tends to sickness. Justice for the worker is a truly religious objective: it follows from the "second commandment," "Thou shalt love thy neighbor as thyself."

2. *Rest, Relaxation, Recreation:* Love for our neighbor helps him find opportunity for rest, relaxation, and recreation. These have genuine health values; and religion promotes them. I quite agree with my friend who said, "I play tennis as part of my religious duty." It helped him keep physically fit while spending many hours a day at missionary work; and I think it helped him have a more wholesome spirit in his work as a Christian minister. I shared his idea so fully that I played tennis with him as often as I could—we even missed prayer-meetings for tennis. In lectures to new missionaries I often urged them to make time for play, for recreation, as a duty they owed to God. If a locomotive has to have time for rest between runs to give it a long life, surely these bodies of ours must have rest: this is part of the way we glorify God with our bodies.

We need to relax, to rest; and I think religion helps us do so. We see people who cannot sit in a chair relaxed; they keep their toes lifted and legs tense. Some even keep up muscular tension as they lie in bed, as if they feared the bed would not hold them. We need to relax, to let go our tension. We need to learn the lesson of the Negro woman who was a hundred years old: when asked the secret of long life, she replied, "When Ah sets, Ah sets looselike." We will live longer and better when we release the strain and tension of our muscles—the muscles are tense because our minds are tense and ill at ease, anxious.

We all need hobbies to express the creative urge in us, to satisfy something innate in man. Hobbies can be truly re-creation. I think all of us should have something to make or do. This is one of the evils of our modern spectator habit—we do nothing but watch others perform. Reading is good, and I truly believe in it: but it is not active, and will not pass for a hobby. I believe in reading just for enjoyment, as well as for profit, for learning. I am one of those who read novels and detective stories for enjoyment, and I think they do me good. And I also read poetry to enjoy the beauty of it, the thrill of it; I think these things make for health, and so are religious. I am glad our churches are encouraging hobbies and recreations, and providing helps for people to get them, as part of their religious service.

Music has two values for us: as listeners, and as performers; for most of us it must be listening. Music does me good in the sheer enjoyment of it; it does much to set the mood of my spirit. Great music lifts my soul and inspires me, and it calms and rests me. I have often come home tired, tense, and even depressed, and been lifted by music. Music from the phonograph that I can choose, or it may be what the radio offers at the time, quickly relieves tension and strain, it rests me. This is even more true of great sacred music. And music inspires and gives me new strength. (I believe we have only begun faintly to realize the therapeutic value of music in our hospitals and sick rooms.)

All these things that help us rest and relax, that give us recreation, are "means of grace" to me, God-given. I am convinced they have been a help to me in healthy living, a help to "glorify God in my body." They have religious values as they have health values. But there is a deeper sense in which I want to use the word "rest."

3. *"Rest in the Lord"*: This is a religious resource for healthy living that is too much neglected by too many of us. It has truly great power in preventing ills, and in healing our sicknesses. Not only does faith in the Lord help us really to relax and rest better; it releases tension and strain, and thus gives better health. Much, if not most, of the tension of the majority of us, is due to self-centeredness, thinking of what events and things will mean to us, what we personally will get from our own actions and from what others may do. The very central thing in this rest in the Lord is turning to Him, and away from self.

We need to take time to rest *"in the Lord"* as we take time to rest our bodies. We may call it a "quiet time," a time for "devotions," a time for prayer; it is the time we consciously spend to realize the presence of God and rest our souls in Him. Some of the busiest men, men who have changed the course of history, have said that when they anticipated an extra busy or hard day, they had to take extra time for quiet devotions and prayer, and I think their unusual accomplishments are in part due to this practice. One of my missionary friends told me just a short time ago, that the time he takes early in the day to be with the Lord is what gives him strength to carry on. He carries a heavy load of responsibilities, and he was feeling the strain of it and getting stale physically; then he gave more time to rest in the Lord, and he has found new energies. I will only mention how E. Stanley Jones says that his physical strength has been sustained for many years of strenuous work by the practice of the quiet time, by the sustaining power of the Lord.

Testimonies as to the value of this quiet religious practice might be cited by thousands. Dr. Peale tells of a business man who takes a short time off each morning at eleven o'clock, and each afternoon at four; he goes away from everyone, and gives his thoughts to God; he does not pray, he thinks about God, and affirms his presence and strengthening; this gives him a "pick-up" far superior to anything he had ever tried before.[2] I am convinced that we would have better health and be more efficient persons if we took time to "rest in the Lord" as regularly as we do to rest.

Muriel Lester tells about a "prayer of relaxation"[3] that she has been practicing; and she is living proof of its value. Miss Lester had been living on her nerves, and had given out; she had been under a doctor's care for seven or eight months; every time she seemed to be a little better and tried to work, she had a relapse. One day her masseuse remarked that Miss Lester did not have the temperament to get well. These comments set Miss Lester to thinking seriously: "I had been ill a long time. The nerves of my heart had apparently struck work; my breathing was irregular, jerky; my heart would miss a beat, and then race along like an engine. If I was interested in a play or conversation, or in anything, my toes would curl up inside my shoes, my fingers would tighten up as though my hand was clenched. If I was reading, my face muscles would become tense. Whenever I was doing anything, I was physically strung up. Now all these habits had to be tackled, undone, every muscle had to be relaxed and accustomed to the state of relaxation. This state had to be recognized as one's normal state, God's will for

[2] Norman Vincent Peale, *A Guide to Confident Living*, pp. 71 f. (Prentice-Hall, New York, 1948).

[3] Muriel Lester, *Ways of Praying*, pp. 20 ff. (Abingdon-Cokesbury Press, Nashville).

one, peace, placidity, leisureliness. . . . I knew I could recover my freshness both physically and spiritually as soon as I could become receptive to the all-pervading power of God. So for an hour each day I would set myself the definite task of gaining renewal of vitality from God by relaxation."

Her method was to be alone and uninterrupted; then to lie down and relax every muscle: she began with fingers and hands and arms; then with toes and feet; then with face muscles. It was hard to get all these muscles to relax completely, and she often had to go back and start over again. When she was relaxed, her breathing would become slow and regular, and a feeling of being so tired all over slowly gave place to a feeling of deep restfulness. With every breath she felt as if she were "breathing in the very breath of God." The amazing vitality and energy of Miss Lester since that time is due to the fact that she has learned to rest in the Lord. She probably does not now have to practice such a routine for relaxation; but whether it takes an hour or only a few moments at a time, she does practice this prayer of relaxation, to rest in the Lord; and those who know her thank God for what she has taught us.

4.*Church-going:* Another method of learning to rest in the Lord is that of attending church; not just to hear the sermon or to hear the choir sing—good though these may be. Go to church to worship and commune with God and His people. Let the music rest or inspire our spirits; let the prayers uplift our souls to feel the presence of God; let the words of Scripture be a message to each one of us; find something in the sermon that will help. Let the problems and troubles of the week be laid aside, let them "simmer," and even if there be times when none of the formal parts of the church program proves helpful, let us turn our thoughts to God and open minds and hearts to Him, think on Him, rest in Him—and we will say that it was good to go unto the house of the Lord, and into His presence.

The very presence of others in a worshipping congregation inspires one; the uplift of music by choir and, even more, joining with the people in hymns, makes God more real; our own prayers are helped by the praying of fellow worshippers, a kind of psychic sharing. Church-going makes us more socially minded; takes us somewhat out of ourselves and our petty concerns; it helps us love our neighbors. And it helps us love God our Father.

I have already referred to the statement of Link, the psychologist, that he found religious, church-going people, on the average, had better personalities than those who did not go to church. As a psychologist he was advising people to "return to religion." [4] One of his reasons for advising people to go to church was that it was a self-discipline, doing what we did not feel inclined to do. The social value was another of his reasons; but the main reason for his insistence was that church-going actually made better personalities. It has been our thesis that mental health, good personality, makes for better health, physical as well as spiritual.

To get the good out of church-going, we should not be only occasional attendants, but regular goers; and we should participate in the services, not just be onlookers. Join in the singing of the hymns, join in the responses with the congregation, follow the prayers thoughtfully; let the spirit of worship possess you, even if the sermon does not interest you. If what is said and done does not appeal to you, turn your thoughts to God in the quiet of your own heart—and you will be helped in your church-going. Make it a habit to go to church.

5. *Use of the Bible:* We all know that the use of the Bible is one of the ways to maintain the religious life of faith. To realize

[4] Link, *op. cit.,* pp. 5 ff.

the values of the Bible, we must acquaint ourselves with it, know it. This demands more than a formal reading of a chapter a day, or reading the Bible through. There is both a study of the Bible by which we learn what it is and what is in it and what it means, and also a devotional use of the Bible. I will not try to make any distinction between our health use and the devotional use of the Bible: health comes from its devotional use. We find the verses and chapters that have meaning for ourselves; and it is a good idea to read the Bible looking for the message it has for us, for ourselves. Then having found it, even though we may have read only a verse or two or have had to read more, take this verse or verses or the message of it and think about it, fix it in the mind; "learn it by heart," memorize the verse and hold it in the heart; it will be there when needed. This is what the Psalmist meant when he said, "Thy word have I hid in my heart, that I might not sin against Thee." [5]

We recognize the power and value of suggestion for mental and physical health: what better suggestion could there be than thus learning Bible verses by heart? In the next section, I refer to some of the Bible verses that I use for myself—along with the words of hymns. I find no better method to help me keep the Lord in my mind, though it may be subconscious at times. I use Bible verses to sustain and vivify my faith, and keep love alive and active.

Dr. Peale made an interesting suggestion to one of the people who consulted him; the man was full of conflicts and anxieties, and some hates and resentments. When his story of irritations and troubles had been poured out, Dr. Peale suggested that it would be a wonderful thing to take out of his mind all the things that were troubling him, like a surgeon making a hole in the skull and scraping them out; but he suggested that it would be

[5] Psalm 119:11.

a good thing to have a minister at hand to put in some Bible verses as good thoughts in place of the troublesome ones taken out. Then he told the man that there are two openings into the mind, the eye and the ear; these can be used to put Bible verses into the mind, and thus prevent the mind filling up with anxieties, resentments, troubles, and conflicts. The man went home and read his Bible to find thoughts to store in his mind, to memorize; these became healing thoughts, and prevented destructive thoughts filling his mind.[6]

This way of using the Bible helps us to keep our minds stayed on the Lord; it helps our faith, it turns us from being self-centered; it makes for better health for the whole man, body and soul. I am sure one of the reasons for the growth of Christianity in Korea, as I saw it, was the fine living of the Korean Christians, their spiritual victories, their better home life, and their better health. The Korean Christians were great students of the Bible as they had it then, memorizing it and practicing it: one of them said he could memorize the Sermon on the Mount verses when he practiced them on his neighbors. It seemed to me that the way the Koreans put the Bible in their hearts was one of the great reasons for the fine example of religious living they set before their neighbors and for the spread of Christianity in that land.

I am sure that the value of some of the cults lies in this positive filling of the mind with good thoughts, health thoughts, success thoughts, victory thoughts; and there is no way better to fill the mind with good thoughts than to put Bible verses into it—learn them by heart. The great Bible verses of faith, hope, confidence, and God's will for us, really help in daily living. I am not saying this as a theory, for they have been in my own life

[6] Peale, *op. cit.*, p. 33.

of more value than I can ever say; they have sustained my faith and hope, maintained courage and confidence, and inspired high ideals for life; and it has always been the verses that I have learned by heart to use in times of need that have thus been of help to me.

6. *"Fear not: Have Faith in God":* It is genuine faith in God that enables one to "rest in the Lord," and it also takes out the strain and eases the tensions and anxieties of daily living, as well as helping us through the crises of life. The tensions and pressures of these times, the pace at which we live, the fears and uncertainties and worries that fill so many hearts, are recognized as being the main factor in many of our ills. Too much work and stress, high tension, and too little relaxation and rest, probably cause more illness among people over forty than germs; we have pretty effectively limited the germ diseases, but we are falling prey to the degenerative diseases—"wearing out."

We may be amused at the comment of a French writer who visited America in 1830: "The American is so restless that he has even invented a chair, called a rocking chair, in which he can move while he sits." But we must admit the truth of his characterization of our tension. I do not mean to imply that I disapprove of rocking chairs: I enjoy a good rocking chair and truly relax; yet I have seen many people who were strenuous even in their rocking.

I think the real basis of this tension and pressure in our living is anxiety or fear, down in the unconscious. Dr. Peale quotes a distinguished physician: "The commonest and subtlest of all human diseases is fear." This does not, of course, refer to normal fear that makes us cautious and careful; it is the abnormal fear that causes so much illness, as we have already seen. I believe religion is the cure and preventive of this fear; and faith in God

is its essence. When we have done our part, we need to trust God for the results. "Commit thy way unto Him, trust also in Him, and He shall bring it to pass" (Psalm 37:5).

Some years ago, I made a study of the health record of missionaries in Korea: it was somewhat surprising to find that there were fewer who had to leave the field because of infectious diseases than because of nervous breakdowns. Some nervous condition was by far the most common cause of health furloughs. These religious workers did not avail themselves of the resources for health inherent in their religion, available to all. Soon after, it was my privilege to be the preacher for a congregation of these missionaries, and I stressed this need for faith that relieves our tensions and gives us peace within, from the text: "Thou wilt keep him in perfect peace whose mind is stayed on Thee, because he trusteth in Thee." [7] This is a faith that keeps the mind stayed on God, instead of on the work and concerns of our own lives, on the Lord rather than on self. We are too prone to feel that everything depends on us, that even the Lord's work must fail if we do not do it, and strenuously. I have reason to think that sermon did a little good, that it was a call to such faith in God that some of us have practiced it more effectively—at least the preacher has.

I have often thought of the word of David Livingstone in his diary, at a time when he was in serious danger from savages threatening to kill him and all his party: "Felt much turmoil of spirit in view of having all my plans for the welfare of this great region and teeming population knocked on the head by savages tomorrow. But I read that Jesus came and said, 'All power is given unto me. . . . Go ye, therefore, and teach all nations— and lo, I am with you alway, even unto the end of the world.' It is the word of a gentleman of the most sacred and strictest

[7] Isaiah 26:3.

honor, and there's an end on it. I will not cross furtively by night as I intended. It would appear as flight, and should such a man as I flee? Nay, verily, I shall take observations for latitude and longitude tonight, though they may be the last. I feel quite calm now, Thank God." [8] I have no doubt that it was this faith and trust in God that enabled Livingstone to carry on so valiantly for the many years.

Religion is the cure for fear, as it brings faith and confidence, trust in God. But one must say that the religion which gives this faith that overcomes fear, is not just an intellectual religion; it is a religion put into practice, a religion of experience rather than of theology. How then shall we attain this faith? To me the answer is given in the verse quoted a short time ago: "Thou wilt keep him in perfect peace whose mind is stayed on Thee, because he trusteth in Thee." It is the mind "stayed on God" that achieves peace and overcomes fears. The word of Brother Lawrence is another way of putting it: "Practice the presence of God."

Having the mind stayed on God, practicing the presence of God, necessitates starting the very first thing in the day. We can form the habit of having thoughts of God with us in the first waking moments. This need not be a formal prayer; it is rather just a turning of our attention to Him, even as we go about the activities of the morning. It may be a thought of appreciation of the beauty of morning when we see the sunshine and brightness of the new day; or if the day is not fair, it may be a thought of His goodness in providing for our needs and comforts, for our homes and those who love us; or it may be a thought of what the Lord is to our world and to ourselves. Surely, the breakfast time is one for thanks and prayer that we

[8] W. G. Blaikie, *Personal Life of David Livingstone*, p. 197 (Fleming H. Revell Co., New York, 1880).

may feel Him with us all the day. There are moments even in our busy days that we may turn our thoughts to the Lord.

While we go about our daily duties and work, we must give attention to those things: but I believe we can have Him in our hearts even in the busiest times. Our ideas of the subconscious mind afford a reasonable explanation of how this can be. It is like a lover who says that there is not a moment day or night but his beloved is in his heart; the thought is not always conscious, but it is there in the depths all the time. When no other matters demand attention, thoughts of the beloved rise to the conscious mind and fill it. In the same way, God is in our hearts and very often in our conscious thoughts as we go about the duties of the day.

And at the end of the day, we may turn the last thoughts of the day to Him, and go to sleep with Him in our hearts. If we will thus practice the presence of God, our minds will be stayed on Him; and the joy of the Lord will fill our hearts. It will be with us as it was with Brother Lawrence, that we find the set times of prayer not different from other times. Brother Lawrence said "that he was more united to God in his outward employments than when he left them for devotions and retirement."

I find that for myself memorized verses of Scripture and hymns help me greatly in keeping my mind stayed on the Lord, consciously and subconsciously. I use them to remind me of His love, His goodness, His power, and His gifts. "Fear thou not, for I am with thee; be not dismayed, for I am thy God; I will strengthen thee; yea, I will help thee; yea, I will uphold thee with the right hand of my righteousness" (Is. 41:10). "If a man love me, he will keep my word: and my Father will love him, and we will come unto him and make our abode with him" (John 14:23). "Lo, I am with you always, even unto the end of the world" (Mat. 28:20). "I have been crucified with Christ, and it is no longer I that live, but Christ liveth in me . . . who loved me and gave Himself up for me" (Gal. 2:20). One could go on almost indefinitely quoting verses that help us to keep our hearts and minds in the knowledge and love of God.

I find the words and tunes of hymns running through my mind a great deal; I do not often sing aloud, but hymns are very often with me: such as "O Love that wilt not let me go . . ." "Dear Lord and Father of mankind . . ." "O Master, let me walk with Thee . . ." "O Jesus Master, when today, I meet along the crowded way my burdened brother . . ." "For the beauty of the earth, For the glory of the skies . . ." "God that madest earth and heaven . . ." "Spirit of God, descend upon my heart. . . ."

It is not alone these personal hymns; the more social hymns that demand thoughts of our brothers are very often singing themselves to me, in me: "Joyful, joyful, we adore Thee, God of glory, Lord of love," sung to the soul-lifting strains of Beethoven's Hymn to Joy from the Ninth Symphony. "God of grace and God of glory, on Thy people pour Thy power . . ." "How firm a foundation . . ." "O brother man, fold to thy heart thy brother . . ." "Where cross the crowded ways of life. . . ." The "Hallelujah Chorus" is hardly in the class of hymns, but it is often with me, to uplift and inspire me, especially in dark times.

I am sure it is more profitable for me to have these hymns and Scripture words as conscious and subconscious thoughts in my mind, than it would be to be anxious about many things. If there were no more to it than crowding out fears and worries, it is worth while to store our minds and hearts with these religious words and thoughts. It has been the "word hid in my heart" that has helped me most. I like the old way of saying it, "to learn by heart" is better than just to memorize Bible verses or hymns. This is making the Bible our own, so that we can say from the heart, "The Lord is my shepherd; I shall not want. . . ."

There is another line of thought we need in our considera-tion of how we are to achieve the faith that overcomes fears: we are not to keep on asking God to give us peace; we are to receive what He is ready to give. He promises peace to the mind stayed on Him; and the Master said, "My peace I give unto you." It is not achieved by striving; it is rather a free gift, like happiness which cannot be attained by seeking it. We use the little faith we have, and God increases our faith; we have faith in God, and take the next step—"I do not ask to see the distant scene, One step enough for me. . . . Lead Thou on. . . ." When we have asked God to give us peace, the next step is to re-ceive it—to have faith that He is giving it. We should not be like the man Dr. Peale called an expert asker, but a poor receiver. It is no good to keep on asking and never practicing the art of receiv-ing. Dr. Peale suggested to a man that he put his watch on the table and ask for peace, praying for two minutes; then he was to thank God for two minutes for doing what he had asked. Three years later the man said he still used his watch, but that the ask-ing took only a half minute, and left him three and a half minutes for thanks.[9]

And it is important that we do not become self-centered in this seeking for peace or for any other blessing sought for our lives. Active religious service for others is one of the best ways to maintain peace for ourselves—once we are right with God. The way of faith working through love is the best way for a wholesome religious life, and this gives freedom from fear: "perfect love casts out fear." Love for our fellows is a pre-ventive of fear; love of God is the perfect cure. It is like a little

<hr>

[9] Peale, *op. cit.*, pp. 142 ff.

child on its mother's lap or in its father's arms; the child's trust and love cast out any fear. So we should be as children of our Father in heaven. "God is love," and we can trust Him!

Our belief in the reality of God helping those who trust Him, who have faith in Him, is no new unusual thing: it is the testimony of great souls through the ages. The Psalmists told of their experiences; and the Bible is full of it: we should remember that the Bible grew out of experience. It was out of the lessons of life that the psalmist said, "The Lord is my shepherd. . . . Yea, though I walk through the valley of the shadow of death, I will fear no evil." "The Lord is my light and my salvation; whom shall I fear? The Lord is the strength of my life; of whom shall I be afraid?" "God is our refuge and strength, a very present help in trouble. Therefore will we not fear."

One of the most frequently used words of the Master was "Fear not." He said, "Be not anxious . . . for your heavenly Father knoweth that ye have need of all these things. . . . But seek ye first His kingdom and His righteousness; and all these things shall be added unto you." Paul said, "Have no anxiety about anything, but in everything by prayer and supplication let your requests be made known to God. And the peace of God which passes all understanding, will keep your hearts and minds in Christ Jesus"; and "My God will supply every need of yours according to His riches in glory in Christ Jesus."

Religious literature is full of examples of faith overcoming fear; and they are not ancient history. I cherish the memory of an evening in Korea, when a group of us met that great man, Dr. Wilfred Grenfell, and heard him tell of his adventures. By special request he told us the story of his drifting out onto the ocean on an ice-pan; he spent all night there and nearly froze; he killed some of his faithful dogs to make a signal pole, and to wrap himself in their furs. He was finally rescued, snow-blinded, with hands and feet frozen. He says, "I can honestly say that from first to last not a single sensation of fear crossed my mind. My own faith in the mystery of immortality is so untroubled that it seemed almost natural to be passing to the portal of death from an ice-pan. Quite unbidden, the words of an old hymn kept running through my head:

> 'My God, my Father, while I stray
> Far from my home on life's rough way,
> Oh, teach me from my heart to say,
> Thy will be done.' "

If we would achieve this peace of heart and mind, we need to practice the ethical and moral teachings of religion, and hold onto intellectual faith. But this is not enough: we must put into actual practice the teachings of religion as to faith and trust. This is probably the hardest part of religious faith to carry out in daily living. Too many of us are like the minister who had a nervous breakdown, and put himself under the care of a doctor. After a thorough examination and many tests, the doctor told him that "if he would practice Christianity he would get well." In reply to his indignant demand to know what the doctor meant, he got the answer: "I suppose you never really read the New Testament. . . . You read it but you do not believe it." The minister fairly shouted, "I do believe it!" Then the doctor said, "Well, let's put it another way—and come now, admit it—you don't really practice its teaching of faith and trust, do you? I know you practice its morals and ethics, but you do not practice your religion in your thought life. Put into mental practice these principles: 'Take no thought for the morrow,' or 'Let not your heart be troubled,' 'Come unto me . . . and I will give you rest.' " Thus the medical man taught the minister to put his religion into practice, and it made him a well man, and a radiant Christian.[10] Religious faith works when it is put into practice!

7. *Forgive: hold no hates:* We have already seen what harm anger and hate can do to our bodies—as well as to our spirits; ill-will poisons the one who holds it more than it harms the other person. It is too much to expect that we can go through life without suffering some wrongs and injuries; but I am sure that if we ourselves have geniune goodwill, the wrongs will not be so many, and people will manifest more goodwill toward us. Too often we misinterpret the words and actions of others as intentional wrongs, when they are innocent of any such intent; and when people do things against us, it is often because they do not understand us or what they do. In any case, we do ourselves an injury when we are not magnanimous and forgiving.

Great souls are magnanimous—that is what the word means. There is no quality revealed in the life of Abraham Lincoln that has so endeared him to the hearts of mankind as this great spirit; we think of how he won over his bitter critic, Edwin M. Stanton, to a deep and abiding friendship by his magnanimity, his forgiving spirit. Lincoln is quoted as saying, "No man resolved to make the most of himself can spare time for personal contention. Still less can he afford to take all the consequences, including the vitiating of his temper, and the loss of self-control." His words, "With malice toward none, with charity for all," mark him as one of the world's greatest souls. And I am sure that this spirit was not just a natural thing for him; it came out of his deep religious feeling, out of his prayer-life.

It is not simply that if we want to be great, we must have this spirit: we dare not allow hate, grudges, and ill-will to spoil our lives, spiritual and physical. Booker T. Washington was right: "I will not let any man reduce my soul to the level of hatred."

[10] *Ibid.,* pp. 168 ff.

It does reduce the fine quality of life to harbor this poison; it may result in ill health to hold on to hostile feelings.

This forgiving, magnanimous spirit does not come by personal cultivation and will-power; it is a fruit of religion. It is when we realize that we are children of the heavenly Father who makes His sun rise on the evil and the good, and sends His rain on the just and the unjust, that we too can forgive. It was not a counsel of perfection when the Master said, "Love your enemies, do good to those who hate you." He was teaching us the way to the good life. He Himself practiced it; and His followers have tried to follow in His steps—many have succeeded. I believe God gives power to us as we try to be of this spirit. I have cited instances of it; I want to add another:

One of my friends in Korea, a Korean minister whom I knew for years, was an example of the way God enables us to maintain this spirit. He was converted to Christianity from a life of fighting, brawling, drunkenness, and lust; he showed such a changed spirit that he was made leader of a small church on one of the islands off the coast of Korea. He was there at the time the Japanese took over his country, made the king of Korea a subject of the Mikado, and put down all signs of resistance with military thoroughness and brutality. The government of his country was taken over by the Japanese, a race at whose hands the Koreans had suffered for centuries—the Koreans hated the Japanese more than Irish Sinn Feiners hated the English. This Korean preacher was a patriot, he bitterly resented the betrayal of his country; he found a group of men of like mind; they armed themselves with long knives and started for the capital, Seoul, each prepared to use his knife to kill an enemy of his country, and then die a martyr. On the way, they went by a certain missionary's house, and this leader went in to say good-by; his twenty companions with their long knives hidden under their long coats waited outside for him. He revealed the plan and purpose; the missionary reminded him of the Master's word about loving enemies, and made him realize that as a Christian he could not do what he proposed. Finally, they were both down on their faces in prayer, and this man yielded his hate to the Lord. He then went out and faced his twenty companions with their long knives: instead of killing him as a betrayer of their plans, under his persuasion, all went back home with their twenty long knives unused. I saw this man as he met Japanese in a friendly way many times in the years following. I found him one of the finest Christians I have known; I can never forget some of the sermons I heard him preach. Truly he received power to love enemies and to pray for them; and I think this made him the fine Christian man I knew and admired.

Probably none of us will ever face the temptation to hate our enemies as this Korean preacher did. But like him, we dare not let hate poison our lives. I recall once that I was sorely tempted to anger and ill-feeling: a man called me on the telephone and strongly blamed me for failures that were not mine but those of my associates. He was hard on me in his anger, and I felt my resentment rising. I paused a moment, then asked him if I might come and see him and talk it over. I took time for a brief, earnest prayer; when I got there and we met, the man was courteous, I recognized that he had cause for grievance, and he recognized that it was not my fault. We had a pleasant interview and a clearer understanding. I am sure the Lord helped to save us both from bitter feelings as we faced the problem together. I do not mean to imply that is the only time I have been so tried; nor can I say that I have always won out over ill-feeling so well; but I do know that when I have let persons or things arouse anger in me, I have been the one who suffered for it in my own spirit and life. Of course, love is the antidote to ill-will; and we can have love as we have fellowship with God, who is love.

8. *Carry No Load of Guilt*: The feeling of guilt may truly be likened to a load; it is a heavy burden. With his burden of sins on his back, the poor pilgrim of Bunyan had a desperately hard time to get out of the Slough of Despond—indeed, he had to have help. Bunyan's story is truly a parable for us: the load of guilt often makes us fall into despondency, unrest, and anxiety. And as we have already seen, it often plunges the burden-bearer into such misery that his health is impaired.

The feeling of guilt often troubles people who do not think of religion and who may have no religious associations in their minds. It may come in the ordinary course of our daily relations with our fellows, in the home, in business, or in the life around us. With the idea that we have offended against the Lord as well as against our fellows, the feeling of guilt is reinforced; but guilt feelings often have no reference to God or His laws or His will. But the guilt feeling is real, whether or not there is any sense of sin against God. We may not feel that a wrong done to a brother is a wrong before the Lord; we may not feel that "inasmuch as ye did it unto one of the least of these, ye did it unto Me"—yet shame for what we have done may weigh us down.

The common-sense thing is that when we feel guilty, we should make it right with our brother, and thus overcome our guilt. Sometimes this cannot be done; but we must not allow ourselves to shirk it just because of the humiliation of an apology and an attempt to achieve a reconciliation. If we have reason to believe that another is hurt by what we have done, we dare not fail to seek reconciliation. Yet we must not hurt people with our efforts to get burdens off our chests at their expense. As was said on an earlier page, each case must be decided on its own merits: but we must honestly face up to ourselves, and make things right when it can be done; we must get rid of the load of guilt.

I have been emphasizing the idea of being reconciled to our fellows; this is what the Master said: "So if you are offering your gift at the altar, and remember that your brother has something against you, leave your gift there before the altar and go; first be reconciled to your brother, and then come and offer your gift." [11] Not even a religious duty, offering, prayer, or worship, can come before our duty to a brother. But this does not mean that there is no place for religion in helping us get release from our load of guilt; and it is doubly true that we must have the help of religion in those cases where we cannot go to the brother to make things right. We have no one else to whom we can go when the way to a brother is closed, we must seek forgiveness of God.

There is practical wisdom in going to a counsellor for help when we have guilt feelings: the counsellor may help us to see how we can right wrongs done, how we can avoid hurting others by our blundering efforts to get it off our chests, how we can receive the pardon of the Lord and make a fresh start. And there is also a value in unburdening our souls to a sympathetic listener; the very telling may clear it up for us so we know what to do; and a "sorrow shared is a sorrow halved." I believe a counsellor who will point us to God and help us to realize His love and help is the best counsellor—and he will not ignore the responsibility we have toward our fellows.

An important thing about finding relief from these loads of guilt is simple faith in the love of a heavenly Father, so that we will accept His forgiveness—and then forgive self. There is no reason for continued agonizing prayers for forgiveness when

[11] Matthew 5:23-24.

we have done our part: the Father is waiting to receive us back into fellowship and love—even as the father of the prodigal son was waiting, watching, and saw him "while he was yet afar off." Then we are not to keep going back in memory and digging up past sins and feeling guilty about them—humble, yes, but not guilty. When we have confessed our wrongs and sins to our brother, to a counsellor, to God, it is ours to accept release from guilt. When we have done what we could, there is no reason for continued guilt feeling.

I think we ought to be free to seek the help of religious counsellors, ministers; and this is one of the very best services the church can render in the way of helping people live healthy, happy lives. There is common sense in the remark of a doctor that people ought to be as free to go to their ministers as they are to a doctor; clergymen are professional men, they know how to keep confidences, and they know how to give good advice—and many of them know how to be good listeners.

In this discussion I have been referring to guilt in the conscious mind, such as normal healthy people feel over errors, failures, and wrongs done in daily living. That is why I have emphasized the need for reconciliation and the righting of wrongs done so far as may be possible; along with this I have stressed the need to remember that we sin against the Father when we do wrong to one of His children, and thus we need to seek His forgiveness. When we have done this, we may, like Bunyan's pilgrim, see our load of guilt roll away. The Lord is gracious: He will cleanse us from guilt.

I realize that there is a great deal of subconscious guilt—repressed hates and resentments that produce feelings of guilt. Not many of us would be capable of a "self-analysis" adequate to deal with these guilt complexes; they take such varied forms, and varied symptoms and signs, that we need the help of a trained consultant. I have already given a good deal of consideration to this phase of the guilt feeling, in the preceding chapter. Here our emphasis is on the guilt "feeling" and not the guilt "complex." We must not carry these loads of guilt; we can be reconciled to a brother whom we have wronged in many cases; and we can have the help of the Lord in living better lives, more kind and more loving, when it is wiser to let our misdeeds be things of the past. I think it well to get the help and counsel of someone trained for this; and I believe religion can be of inestimable value to any who feel guilt.

9. *Prayer—Practicing the Presence of God:* I have no intention of presenting a comprehensive discussion of the vast subject of prayer; it is my purpose only to present a few ideas as to the use of prayer in healthy living—not so much prayers for health, as prayers that make for a wholesome, healthy life of body and soul.

I have already spoken of the prayer of relaxation, of rest in the Lord, prayers of faith that keep us from fears and anxieties, prayers for forgiveness, prayers for power to love—as well as prayers for healing and for comfort. I do not want to discuss the matter of petitions for things needed or desired, nor intercessory—though I believe in them. I want rather to present prayer as a way of realizing the presence of God, as communion with Him, and as a way of receiving His guidance in our living and of committing ourselves to Him in confidence and faith.

I can never forget the impression made upon me and the thousands of other Student Volunteers at the Nashville convention in 1906, when Bishop Thoburn, of India, walked out on the platform and said to us: "Jesus Christ is standing by my side here this morning, just as really as you young folk in the audience before me. He was with me when I went aboard ship to go to India, and when I walked down the gangplank forty-seven years ago; and He has been with me all the time from that day to this." This may not be a literal quotation, it is from memory many years later. I know I could almost see the Master standing beside that white-haired old missionary; and I have never doubted the reality of His presence even though my eyes did not see Him. He was too real to Bishop Thoburn for us to suspect any illusions about it. That man's life was lived in the presence of God, as I have longed to do and never attained. He truly prayed without ceasing.

It is when we live "practicing the presence of God" that we may expect Him to guide us. There has been much written about "guidance," some wise and some not wise. But I believe that if we live in His presence, we may expect Him to lead us just as fully as we can realize His will for us and just as far as we are willing to go. I do not mean by this that He directs the little petty details of our daily lives; we have what He gave us of reason and intelligence, they are for us to use. It cost me a great deal of prayer and thought, but I became as certainly convinced that I was doing His will for me in becoming a medical missionary—as much as I can be convinced of anything. This gave me a confidence in my work that I cannot overestimate; I did not have to worry about whether I was in the work I should be doing, and it relieved me of fear that I was in the wrong job. That is not the only time I have felt that He has led me—though there were dark times of uncertainty, as changes have come with the years, especially when I had to leave Korea in ill health, and later take up other work in the homeland. This fruit of prayer and confidence has meant much to me through the years; it has helped me to do the best I could to the limit of my ability, and then leave the results to the Lord.

This belief in prayer and guidance does not mean that I think we are to be hasty or foolish. Stanley Jones is right in saying that we need to be alert to God's many ways of guiding us, and not be led into lightly thinking He directs all our petty doings. We must test our ideas by what we know of the will of God as revealed in the life of the Master, in the teachings of the Bible, by the good counsel of friends, and by just good common sense. But there is a guidance of the Lord by His Spirit in our lives, call this what we may. Jones calls it "The Voice." It has never been my practice to take a piece of paper and a pencil, and after prayer and quiet, trust the Lord to guide me in writing a program for the day: some have been blessed by this, if they have used common sense and spiritual wisdom with it. It seems to me that it is rather the achieving of such communion with God that we are in harmony with His will in the great purposes and decisions of life. Then the details fit into the master plan by the use of what judgment the Lord gives us to use.

This prayer for guidance is not so much petition for specific things as it is an endeavor to share His spirit, His attitudes, His love. It is prayer of communion; not just formal prayers, but an abiding sense of the presence of God and His guidance. The emphasis I am trying to make here is that of how it relieves tension and strain in our daily lives, makes life meaningful, and adds to our joys: it makes life more whole, more healthful.

One further thing about prayer as a factor in healthy living. We are bidden to pray for our "daily bread"—for our needs. I cannot go along with those who teach that by prayer we can gain wealth, or power, or influence—except as a by-product of fine religious character. Prayer is no guarantee of even plenty: God's saints, many of them, have suffered want, deprivation, hunger, even unto death. This does not mean that I do not

believe God will give things to those who pray and trust Him—
He does many times, more than we can ask or think. But
His saints have suffered for lack of food and clothing and
shelter: who can assert the contrary in our day, when war has
wrought its desolation and ruin over so much of our world?
I cannot believe that all the sufferers in our wars have been
"sinners above others"; I know some real saints suffering because of the war now going on in Korea, through no fault
of theirs. I do not believe this is the will of the Father: it is the
sin of mankind, our sins against our brothers that have brought
this agony upon them—and we Americans must take our share
of the blame, the sin. But in the midst of it all, the heart of
God bleeds for His suffering children: "Like as a father pitieth
his children."

I have never personally faced such deprivation that I did not
know where the next meal—for those I love and for myself—
would come from; I dare not say how I would react in such a
condition. I have never dared to preach from the text, "My
God will supply every need of yours according to His riches
in glory in Christ Jesus"; my experience of want has not qualified me to do it. Yet I do believe it is true: not that all our
"wants" will be supplied—far from it; and it may be that sometimes physical supplies may be lacking and we may suffer want.
In God's wisdom we may even have to go without "necessities,"
and die—yet our real needs, the needs of the real "I" will be
supplied. The supreme need is not for things, but for God and
fellowship with Him and His people, in life, in death, and beyond death. If by our prayers we can attain this faith in God,
and live in Him, "we will not fear, though the earth do change,
and though the mountains be shaken into the heart of the
seas. . . ." This is the "life hid with Christ in God"; and we

can "know that in everything God works for good with those who love Him."

I believe that this life of prayer, a true religious life, should be a positive help to us for good health: it does not assure us freedom from infections, from chemical or physical injury, from wearing out these body machines of ours; but I believe it will help us stay free of the emotions and tensions that wreak such havoc with health. It is putting ourselves in harmony with the Creator and the God of the ongoing process of life. It gives us resources for living that God offers to us as we live in Him and He in us!

BIBLIOGRAPHY

*Books from which quotations have been taken, or
to which reference has been made without direct
quotation, and others consulted and found valuable.*

1. Medical and Psychological

ALFRED ADLER: *Understanding Human Nature*
———: *What Life Should Mean to You*
GERHARD ADLER: *Studies in Analytical Psychology*
WALTER C. ALVAREZ: *Nervousness, Indigestion, and Pain*
WALTER B. CANNON: *Bodily Changes in Pain, Hunger, Fear and Rage*
———: *The Wisdom of the Body*
FLANDERS DUNBAR: *Emotions and Bodily Changes*
———: *Mind and Body: Psychosomatic Medicine*
———: *Synopsis of Psychosomatic Diagnosis and Treatment*
SIGMUND FREUD: *General Introduction to Psychoanalysis*
JAMES ARTHUR HADFIELD: "The Mind and the Brain," in *Immortality*, by B. H. Streeter and others.
———: "The Psychology of Power," in *The Spirit*, by B. H. Streeter and others
KAREN HORNEY: *Neurotic Personality of Our Time*
———: *Self-Analysis*
WILLIAM HENRY HOWELL: *Text-Book of Physiology*
WILLIAM JAMES: *Psychology—Briefer Course*
———: *Varieties of Religious Experience*
C. G. JUNG: *Modern Man in Search of a Soul*
———: *Psychology and Religion*
HENRY C. LINK: *The Return to Religion*

WILLIAM MCDOUGALL: *Body and Mind*
————: *Outline of Psychology*
WENDELL MUNCIE: *Psychobiology and Psychiatry*
T. A. ROSS: *The Common Neuroses*
WILLIAM S. SADLER: *The Mind at Mischief*
————: *Modern Psychiatry*
JOHN B. WATSON: *Behaviorism*
EDWARD WEISS AND O. SPURGEON ENGLISH: *Psychosomatic Medicine*
CARL J. WIGGERS: *Physiology in Health and Disease*
HAROLD G. WOLFF: "Life Situation, Emotions and Disease," in *Teaching Psychotherapeutic Medicine*, edited by Helen L. Witmer.

II. Religious

SMILEY BLANTON AND NORMAN V. PEALE: *Faith Is the Answer*
JOHN S. BONNELL: *Pastoral Psychiatry*
————: *Psychology for Pastor and People*
CHARLES R. BROWN: *Faith and Health*
JAMES M. BUCKLEY: *Faith-Healing, Christian Science, and Kindred Phenomena*
RICHARD C. CABOT AND RUSSELL L. DICKS: *The Art of Ministering to the Sick*
MRS. MARY BAKER-GLOVER-PATTERSON-EDDY: *Science and Health*
CHARLES FILLMORE: *Christian Healing*
DANA GATLIN: *God Is the Answer*
SEWARD HILTNER: *Religion and Health*
E. STANLEY JONES: *Abundant Living* (and others in series)
————: *Christ of the Indian Road*
————: *Is the Kingdom of God Realism?*
CHARLES F. KEMP: *Physicians of the Soul*
MURIEL LESTER: *It Occurred to Me*
————: *Ways of Praying*
NORMAN VINCENT PEALE: *Guide to Christian Living*

LEWIS SHERRILL: *Guilt and Redemption*

JAMES H. SNOWDEN: *The Truth About Christian Science*

LESLIE WEATHERHEAD: *Psychology and Life*

————: *Psychology in Service of the Soul*

CARROLL A. WISE: *Religion in Illness and Health*

ELWOOD WORCESTER: *Life's Adventure*

————: *Making Life Better*

ELWOOD WORCESTER, SAMUEL MCCOMB, AND I. H. CORIAT: *Religion and Medicine*

STEFAN ZWEIG: *Mental Healers*